D0515462

# ART
## IN THE
## UNITED
## STATES
## CAPITOL

NEG. NO. 27751

FREEDOM
Thomas Crawford
Dome of the United States Capitol

94th Congress, 2d Session                    House Document Number 94–660

# ART
## IN THE
## UNITED
## STATES
## CAPITOL

PREPARED BY
THE ARCHITECT OF THE CAPITOL
UNDER THE DIRECTION OF
THE JOINT COMMITTEE ON THE LIBRARY

UNITED STATES GOVERNMENT PRINTING OFFICE
WASHINGTON 1978

iii

Library of Congress Card Catalog Number 72-600081

For sale by the Superintendent of Documents, U.S. Government Printing Office
Washington, D.C. 20402

Stock No. 052–071–00546–3

H. Con. Res. 698 Passed Oct. 1, 1976

(Submitted by Mr. Brademus)

## Ninety-fourth Congress of the United States of America

### CONCURRENT RESOLUTION

*Resolved by the House of Representatives (the Senate concurring),* That there be reprinted with black and white and color illustrations and with emendations as a House document "Art in the United States Capitol" as prepared under the direction of the Architect of the Capitol; and that there be printed thirty-six thousand four hundred additional copies of such document, of which ten thousand three hundred copies shall be for the use of the Senate, twenty-two thousand one hundred copies shall be for the use of the House of Representatives, and four thousand copies for the use of the Architect of the Capitol.

Attest:

EDMUND L. HENSHAW, JR.
*Clerk of the House.*

Attest:

FRANCIS R. VALEO
*Secretary of the Senate.*

# COMMITTEE ON HOUSE ADMINISTRATION

*Ninety-fourth Congress—Second Session*

FRANK THOMPSON, JR., New Jersey, *Chairman*

JOHN H. DENT, Pennsylvania

LUCIEN N. NEDZI, Michigan

JOHN BRADEMAS, Indiana

AUGUSTUS F. HAWKINS, California

FRANK ANNUNZIO, Illinois

JOSEPH M. GAYDOS, Pennsylvania

ED JONES, Tennessee

ROBERT H. MOLLOHAN, West Virginia

DAWSON MATHIS, Georgia

LIONEL VAN DEERLIN, California

JOSEPH G. MINISH, New Jersey

MENDEL J. DAVIS, South Carolina

CHARLES ROSE, North Carolina

LINDY (MRS. HALE) BOGGS, Louisiana

JOHN L. BURTON, California

EDWARD W. PATTISON, New York

WILLIAM L. DICKINSON, Alabama

SAMUEL L. DEVINE, Ohio

JAMES C. CLEVELAND, New Hampshire

CHARLES E. WIGGINS, California

J. HERBERT BURKE, Florida

W. HENSON MOORE, Louisiana

BILL FRENZELL, Minnesota

RON PAUL, Texas

WILLIAM H. CABLE, *Staff Director and Associate Counsel*

ROBERT E. MOSS, *General Counsel*

# JOINT COMMITTEE ON THE LIBRARY

*Ninety-fourth Congress—Second Session*

HOWARD W. CANNON, Senator from Nevada, *Chairman*

LUCIEN N. NEDZI, Representative from Michigan, *Vice Chairman*

FRANK THOMPSON, JR.
Representative from New Jersey

JOHN BRADEMAS
Representative from Indiana

CLAIBORNE PELL
Senator from Rhode Island

HARRISON A. WILLIAMS, JR.
Senator from New Jersey

SAMUEL L. DEVINE
Representative from Ohio

W. HENSON MOORE
Representative from Louisiana

ROBERT P. GRIFFIN
Senator from Michigan

HUGH SCOTT
Senator from Pennsylvania

WILLIAM McWHORTER COCHRANE, *Chief Clerk*

ROBERT STEWART ROYER, *Assistant Chief Clerk*

# JURISDICTION OVER WORKS OF ART

Since 1872 the Joint Committee on the Library has had supervision of all works of art in the United States Capitol under the provisions of section 1831 of the Revised Statutes of the United States as follows:

The Joint Committee on the Library, whenever, in their judgment, it is expedient, are authorized to accept any work of the fine arts, on behalf of Congress, which may be offered, and to assign the same such place in the Capitol as they may deem suitable, and shall have the supervision of all works of art that may be placed in the Capitol.

# REPRODUCTIONS

Negative numbers in this book are for 8″ x 10″ black and white prints only. They may be purchased by title and negative number from the Photoduplication Service, Library of Congress, Washington, D.C. 20540. Color slides, color prints and color transparencies are not available.

All photographs, with exceptions as noted, are property of the U.S. Government, Office of the Architect of the Capitol, United States Capitol, Washington, D.C. 20515.

# MEASUREMENTS AND SIGNATURE LOCATIONS

Sight measurements of portraits and paintings are given with height first and width second. Measurements of busts and statues are approximate and do not include the pedestals.

The location of the artist's signature is designated by the letters u.l., u.r., l.l., and l.r., indicating upper left, upper right, lower left and lower right.

# THE CAPITOL ART COLLECTION

COMPRISES A TOTAL OF 682 WORKS OF ART AS OF DECEMBER 1976

## 136 PORTRAITS

14 Presidents of the United States
2 Vice Presidents of the United States
22 United States Senators
46 Speakers of the House of Representatives
7 Small portraits of Speakers of the House of Representatives
24 Chairmen of the House Committee on Appropriations
8 Architects of the Capitol
13 Prominent Individuals

## 54 PAINTINGS:

8 in the Rotunda
12 in the Senate wing
5 in the House wing
18 in the Central section
1 in the Russell Senate Office Building
10 in the House Office Buildings

## 77 BUSTS:

10 Presidents of the United States
37 Vice Presidents of the United States
5 Chief Justices of the United States
4 United States Senators
10 Speakers and Members of the House of Representatives
11 Prominent Individuals

## 102 STATUES:

92 contributed by States to the National Statuary Hall collection
9 not contributed by States
1 Liberty and the Eagle
1 Women's Suffrage Monument

## 90 RELIEFS:

75 in the House Chamber:
    23 portraits of Lawgivers, 52 Seals of States and Territories
1 in the Old Supreme Court Chamber
8 in the Rotunda
3 in the Senate Chamber
3 on the East Front portico

## 137 FRESCOES, MURALS AND LUNETTES:

2 in the Rotunda
15 in the House wing
120 in the Senate wing

## 29 EXTERIOR WORKS OF ART:

4 bronze doors
1 fountain
19 statues
1 memorial
4 tympanums

## 57 MISCELLANEOUS WORKS OF ART:

37 sculptures:
    23 capitals, 2 clocks, 2 eagles,
    1 fountain, 1 mask, 2 statuettes,
    2 sculptural groups, 4 stairways.
4 vases
16 windows and laylights:
    7 circular, 7 rectangular,
    1 Prayer Room, 1 Washington memorial.

The objects in Appendix I and Appendix II are not included in this tabulation.

# Foreword

The collection of art in the United States Capitol represents an integral part of the history of this renowned building. This edition of *Art in the United States Capitol* is the culmination of various publications issued over the past seventy years. In 1927, the first comprehensive history of the accumulation and development of art in the Capitol was compiled by art curator Charles E. Fairman. Fairman's chronological narrative, *Art and Artists of the Capitol of the United States of America*, was the forerunner of a twenty-four page catalog issued by the Architect of the Capitol in 1952. The catalog was not illustrated, but because of its thorough and concise listing, the Joint Committee on the Library published it as a joint committee print.

The Capitol art collection continued to grow and public demand for information on the subject increased. As a result, the first hardbound edition on Capitol art was released in 1965, entitled *Compilation of Works of Art and Other Objects in the United States Capitol*. That volume contained over four hundred black and white illustrations of paintings and sculptures, including reliefs, frescoes, plaques and miscellaneous objects of interest and served as a valuable reference tool.

The 1976 Bicentennial edition featured several changes, including the present title. Color photographs of the paintings replaced black and white pictures, enhancing the total beauty and value of the book. The succinct new format provides additional information not previously available in a single volume. Included in the appendix are diagrams that enable students and visitors to locate works of art in which they are interested.

I wish to recognize the particular contributions and interest of the Honorable William L. Dickinson of Alabama for his foresight in introducing the first concurrent resolution for the printing of the 1976 edition and also the Honorable John Brademas of Indiana for his leadership in seeing that the second printing of *Art in the United States Capitol* became a fact.

George M. White, Architect of the Capitol, and members of his staff headed by Florian H. Thayn and her assistant Karen L. Miles of the Art and Reference Division, are responsible for the research, text and general organization of the book. The excellent photographs, both color and black and white, are the work of Harry L. Burnett, Jr. and Mark M. Blair.

*Frank Thompson, Jr.*

FRANK THOMPSON, JR., *Chairman*
Committee on House Administration

HOWARD W. CANNON, NEV., CHAIRMAN

CLAIBORNE PELL, R.I.
ROBERT C. BYRD, W. VA.
JAMES B. ALLEN, ALA.
HARRISON A. WILLIAMS, JR., N.J.
DICK CLARK, IOWA

MARK O. HATFIELD, OREG.
ROBERT P. GRIFFIN, MICH.
HOWARD H. BAKER, JR., TENN.

WILLIAM MC WHORTER COCHRANE, STAFF DIRECTOR
CHESTER H. SMITH, CHIEF COUNSEL
LARRY E. SMITH, MINORITY STAFF DIRECTOR

## United States Senate

COMMITTEE ON
RULES AND ADMINISTRATION
WASHINGTON, D.C. 20510

On behalf of the Senate Committee on Rules and Administration, I am happy to join in sponsoring this new edition of *Art in the United States Capitol*, the first to illustrate most of this notable and historic collection in color. This second printing, the need for which was occasioned by the very gratifying public response to the new edition, incorporates the changes in location or accessions which have occurred during the second session of the Ninety-fourth Congress.

*Howard W. Cannon*

HOWARD W. CANNON
*Chairman*
Senate Committee on Rules
and Administration

x

# Contents

# Portraits

Presidents of the United States
Vice Presidents of the United States
United States Senators
Speakers of the House of Representatives
Chairmen of the House Committee on Appropriations
Architects of the Capitol
Prominent Individuals

NEG. NO. 23105

GEORGE WASHINGTON
William Dunlap, 1783, from life, pastel, 25½″ x 19½″
Gift of Mrs. A. V. H. Ellis, 1940
Accepted by the Joint Committee on the Library
SB–16

NEG. NO. 34613

GEORGE WASHINGTON AT PRINCETON
Charles Willson Peale, 91⅝″ x 58⅜″
Signed l.l. C. W. Peale pinx, Philadelphia 1779
Purchased 1882
Senate wing, third floor, west corridor

3

NEG. NO. 36684

GEORGE WASHINGTON
Rembrandt Peale, 1828, from life, 69½″ x 52½″
Purchased 1832
S–228, Old Senate Chamber

NEG. NO. 24197

GEORGE WASHINGTON
Gilbert Stuart, from life, Thomas Chestnut portrait, 28½″ x 23½″
Purchased 1876
S–207, Senators' Conference Room

5

NEG. NO. 719

GEORGE WASHINGTON
Gilbert Stuart, from life, Lansdowne or "teapot" type, 93″ x 59″
Transferred from U.S. Embassy in Spain to the Capitol, 1951
Placed by authority of the Speaker
H–207, House Reception Room

NEG. NO. 24316

GEORGE WASHINGTON
Gilbert Stuart, from life, Edward Pennington portrait, 30″ x 25″
Purchased 1886
S–210

NEG. NO. 27552

GEORGE WASHINGTON
John Vanderlyn, 1834, after Gilbert Stuart, 92″ x 62″
Commissioned by Resolution of June 28, 1832, 22nd Congress
House Chamber

JOHN ADAMS
BY E. F. ANDREWS

NEG. NO. 23939

JOHN ADAMS
Eliphalet Frazer Andrews, 1881, after Gilbert Stuart, 29½″ x 24½″
Purchased 1881
Senate wing, second floor, main corridor

NEG. NO. 23936

THOMAS JEFFERSON
Thomas Sully, 29½'' x 24½''
Signed on back TS 1856
Purchased 1874
S–210

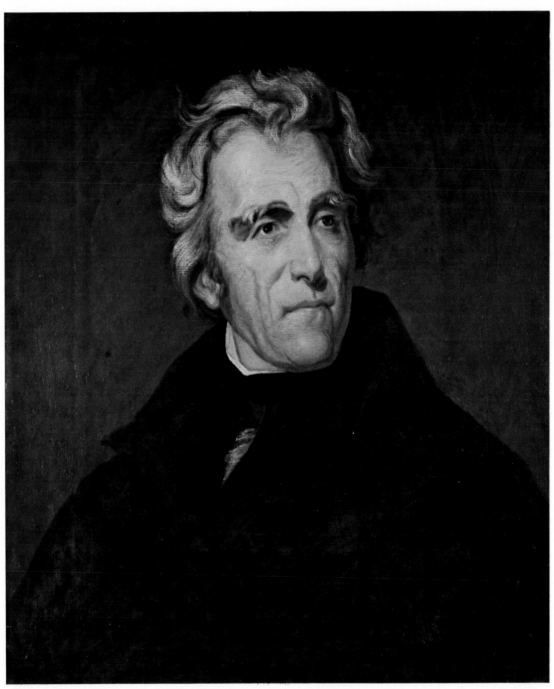

NEG. NO. 23937

ANDREW JACKSON
Attributed to Thomas Sully, 1845, 29½″ x 24½″
Purchased 1922 by S. Res. 75, 67th Congress
S–210

NEG. NO. 34611

ABRAHAM LINCOLN
Antonio Salviati, mosaic, 22″ diameter
Gift of the artist, 1866
Accepted by Con. Res. of July 26, 1866, 39th Congress
S–109

ABRAHAM LINCOLN
BY FREEMAN THORP

NEG. NO. 23938

ABRAHAM LINCOLN
Freeman Thorp, about 1879, 28½″ x 23″
Signed u. r. Thorp
Purchased 1920 by S. Res. 292, 66th Congress
Senate wing, second floor, main corridor

13

NEG. NO. 24317

ULYSSES S. GRANT
William Cogswell, oval, 29½″ x 24″
Signed l. center W. Cogswell, 1868
Purchased 1886
Accepted by the Joint Committee on the Library
S–210

NEG. NO. 34612

JAMES A. GARFIELD
Antonio Salviati, mosaic, 24″ diameter
Signed r. center Dr. A. Salviati, Venezia 1882
Gift of the artist, 1884
Accepted by Con. Res. of May 19, 1884, 48th Congress
S–109

# VICE PRESIDENTS

TWO PORTRAITS

NEG. NO. 39580

JOHN C. CALHOUN
Henry F. Darby, about 1849, 46″ x 36″
Signed l.l. H. F. Darby
Purchased 1881
Senate wing, second floor, main corridor

NEG. NO. 33837

John Nance Garner
Signed 1.1. Howard Chandler Christy, 1937; 53½″ x 39½″
Purchased 1940 by P. L. 723, 75th Congress

NEG. NO. 24358

WILLIAM B. ALLISON
Willbur Aaron Reaser, 41½″ x 33½″
Signed l.r. W. A. Reaser
Purchased 1909 by S. Res. 264, 60th Congress
Senate wing, second floor, main corridor

NEG. NO. 32188

CHARLES CARROLL OF CARROLLTON
Chester Harding, 35½'' x 27½''
Purchased 1870
House wing, third floor, east corridor

NEG. NO. 39581

HENRY CLAY
Henry F. Darby, 50″ x 40″
Signed l.r. H. F. Darby
Purchased 1881
Senate wing, second floor, main corridor

NEG. NO. 32189

HENRY CLAY
Signed l.l. Jno. Neagle, 1843; 9′ x 5′11′′
Purchased 1871
House wing, third floor, east corridor

21

NEG. NO. 25065

JOHN ADAMS DIX
Signed 1.1. Imogene Robinson Morrell, 1883; 50″ x 40″
Purchased 1883
In storage

NEG. NO. 32795

ARTHUR P. GORMAN
Louis P. Dieterich, 45½'' x 33''
Signed l.r. L. Dieterich, 1911
Gift of the Gorman family, 1943
Accepted by the Joint Committee on the Library
S–220

NEG. NO. 25976

JOHN LANGDON
Hattie E. Burdette, 1916, after an engraving, 30″ x 25″
Signed l.r. H. E. Burdette
Purchased 1916 by S. Res. 118, 64th Congress
S–240

24

NEG. NO. 24199

Henry Latimer
Signed l.r. Clawson S. Hammitt; 29½″ x 24½″
Gift of Mary Latimer, 1916
Accepted by the Joint Committee on the Library
Senate wing, third floor, south corridor

NEG. NO. 25977

JAMES HAMILTON LEWIS
Signed u.l. Louis Betts; 39½″ x 29″
Gift of Mrs. Lewis, 1940
Accepted by the Joint Committee on the Library
Senate wing, second floor, south corridor

NEG. NO. 33835

CHARLES L. MCNARY
Henrique Medina, 39½″ x 29½″
Signed u.r. H. Medina, 1946
Gift of friends, 1944
Accepted by the Joint Committee on the Library
Senate wing, second floor, main corridor

27

NEG. NO. 37095

JUSTIN S. MORRILL
Eastman Johnson, 25″ x 21″
Signed l.l. E. Johnson, 1884
Gift of Louise S. Swan, 1920
Accepted by the Joint Committee on the Library
Senate wing, second floor, main corridor

NEG. NO. 25979

JOSEPH T. ROBINSON
Nicholas R. Brewer, 43″ x 31½″
Signed l.l. N. R. Brewer, 1934
Gift of friends, 1937
Accepted by S. Res. 173, 75th Congress
Senate wing, second floor, main corridor

29

NEG. NO. 25980

MORRIS SHEPPARD
Signed l.r. Boris B. Gordon—1941; 41½″ x 33½″
Gift of the Sheppard family, 1941
Accepted by S. Res. 197, 77th Congress
In storage

NEG. NO. 24411

CHARLES SUMNER
Walter Ingalls, 43½'' x 35½''
Signed l.r. W. Ingalls, Pinxt 1876
Purchased 1886
Senate wing, second floor, main corridor

ALLEN G. THURMAN
John H. Witt
Purchased 1896 by S. Res. of January 10, 1896, 54th Congress
Location unknown. No photograph

NEG. NO. 37921

DANIEL WEBSTER
John Neagle, 50″ x 40″
Purchased 1881
Senate wing, second floor, main corridor

NEG. NO. 34274

DANIEL WEBSTER
James Henry Wright, 50″ x 40″
Signed l.r. J. H. Wright, N.Y.
Gift of Lester Martin, 1944
Accepted by S. Res. 330, 78th Congress
Senate wing, stairwell opposite S–216

When Constantino Brumidi decorated the walls of the Senate Reception Room, S–213, in the 1860's, he left unadorned areas for medallion portraits of great men yet to come. In 1956 by special legislation[1] provision was made to have the portraits of five great Senators painted in oil. Each measures 22½″ x 19½″. The unveiling was March 12, 1959.

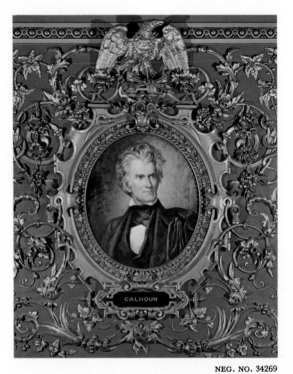

NEG. NO. 34269

John C. Calhoun, South Carolina
Arthur Conrad

---

[1] S. Res. 297, 84th Congress (July 12, 1956) and S. Res. 174, 84th Congress (August 26, 1957).

NEG. NO. 34271

ROBERT M. LA FOLLETTE, SR., Wisconsin
Chester LA Follette

NEG. NO. 34270

HENRY CLAY, Kentucky
Allyn Cox

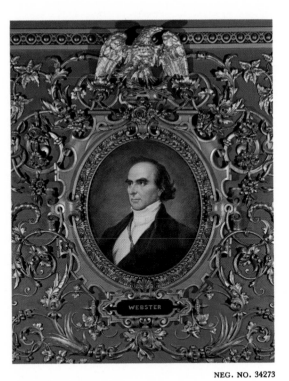

NEG. NO. 34273

DANIEL WEBSTER, Massachusetts
Adrian Lamb

NEG. NO. 34272

ROBERT A. TAFT, Ohio
Deane Keller

# SPEAKERS OF THE HOUSE OF REPRESENTATIVES

## FORTY-SIX PORTRAITS

This collection includes all Speakers of the House of Representatives from Speaker Muhlenberg of the First Congress through Speaker Albert of the Ninety-fourth Congress. These portraits are located in the Speaker's Lobby, House wing, second floor.

In earlier days the portraits of former Speakers were received through donations, but since 1910 provision has been made for the painting of the portrait of each Speaker during his incumbency. These portraits are hung without ceremony, usually at the close of the Speaker's term of office. The payment date is generally used as the date of purchase for this collection. According to Government procedure, the portrait would have been delivered, although it might not have been hung, by the time payment was made.

The chronological list of Speakers is followed by the portraits which are shown alphabetically.

| Speaker | State | Period of service | Artist | Date of acquisition |
|---|---|---|---|---|
| Frederick A. C. Muhlenberg | Pennsylvania | 1789–91; 1793–95 | Samuel B. Waugh after Joseph Wright | 1881 |
| Jonathan Trumbull | Connecticut | 1791–93 | H. I. Thompson | 1880 |
| Jonathan Dayton | New Jersey | 1795–99 | Henry Harrison | 1911 |
| Theodore Sedgwick | Massachusetts | 1799–1801 | Edgar Parker | 1888 |
| Nathaniel Macon | North Carolina | 1801–07 | Robert D. Gauley | 1911 |
| Joseph B. Varnum | Massachusetts | 1807–11 | Charles L. Elliott | 1888 |
| Henry Clay | Kentucky | 1811–14; 1815–20; 1823–25 | Giuseppe Fagnani | 1852 |
| Langdon Cheves | South Carolina | 1814–15 | Hal Morrison | 1912 |
| John W. Taylor | New York | 1820–21; 1825–27 | Caroline L. O. Ransom | 1900 |
| Philip P. Barbour | Virginia | 1821–23 | Kate F. Edwards | 1911 |
| Andrew Stevenson | Virginia | 1827–34 | Spencer B. Nichols | 1911 |
| John Bell | Tennessee | 1834–35 | Willie B. Newman | 1911 |
| James K. Polk | Tennessee | 1835–39 | Rebecca Polk | 1911 |
| Robert M. T. Hunter | Virginia | 1839–41 | Richard N. Brooke | 1911 |
| John White | Kentucky | 1841–43 | Gerard Barry | 1911 |
| John W. Jones | Virginia | 1843–45 | James B. Sword | 1911 |
| John W. Davis | Indiana | 1845–47 | W. D. Murphy | 1911 |
| Robert C. Winthrop | Massachusetts | 1847–49 | Daniel Huntington | 1882 |
| Howell Cobb | Georgia | 1849–51 | Lucy Stanton | 1912 |
| Linn Boyd | Kentucky | 1851–55 | Stanley Middleton | 1911 |
| Nathaniel P. Banks | Massachusetts | 1855–57 | Robert Vonnoh | 1888 |
| James L. Orr | South Carolina | 1857–59 | Esther Edmonds | 1911 |
| William Pennington | New Jersey | 1859–61 | Joseph Lauber | 1911 |
| Galusha A. Grow | Pennsylvania | 1861–63 | William A. Greaves | 1892 |
| Schuyler Colfax | Indiana | 1863–68 | Freeman Thorp | 1911 |
| Theodore M. Pomeroy | New York | 1868–69 | George L. Clough | 1921 |
| James G. Blaine | Maine | 1869–75 | Freeman Thorp | 1905 |
| Michael C. Kerr | Indiana | 1875–76 | Charles A. Gray | 1911 |
| Samuel J. Randall | Pennsylvania | 1876–81 | William A. Greaves | 1892 |
| J. Warren Keifer | Ohio | 1881–83 | Charles A. Gray | 1911 |
| John G. Carlisle | Kentucky | 1883–89 | Ellen D. Hale | 1911 |
| Thomas B. Reed | Maine | 1889–91; 1895–99 | John S. Sargent | 1891 |
| Charles F. Crisp | Georgia | 1891–95 | Robert Hinckley | 1894 |
| David B. Henderson | Iowa | 1899–1903 | Freeman Thorp | 1913 |
| Joseph G. Cannon | Illinois | 1903–11 | William T. Smedley | 1917 |
| Champ Clark | Missouri | 1911–19 | Boris B. Gordon | 1919 |
| Frederick H. Gillett | Massachusetts | 1919–25 | Edmund C. Tarbell | 1925 |
| Nicholas Longworth | Ohio | 1925–31 | Robert Doblhoff | 1930 |
| John N. Garner | Texas | 1931–33 | Seymour M. Stone | 1940 |
| Henry T. Rainey | Illinois | 1933–34 | Howard C. Christy | 1936 |
| Joseph W. Byrns | Tennessee | 1935 | Ella S. Hergesheimer | 1937 |
| William B. Bankhead | Alabama | 1936–39 | Howard C. Christy | 1938 |
| Sam Rayburn | Texas | 1940–46; 1949–52; 1955–61 | Douglas Chandor | 1942 |
| Joseph W. Martin, Jr. | Massachusetts | 1947–48; 1953–54 | Boris B. Gordon | 1959 |
| John W. McCormack | Massachusetts | 1962–71 | Victor Lallier | 1962 |
| Carl B. Albert | Oklahoma | 1971–77 | Charles B. Wilson | 1973 |

NEG. NO. 34301

CARL ALBERT, Speaker
Charles Banks Wilson
Purchased 1973 by Public Law 92–342

NEG. NO. 34302

WILLIAM B. BANKHEAD, Speaker
Signed l.r. Howard Chandler Christy, Feb. 1937; 53″ x 39″
Purchased 1937 by Public No. 4, 75th Congress

NEG. NO. 39579

NATHANIEL P. BANKS, Speaker
Signed l.l. Robt. W. Vonnoh, Boston, 1887; 49″ x 31½″
Gift of State of Massachusetts, 1888
Accepted by H. Res. of January 19, 1888, 50th Congress

41

NEG. NO. 34304

PHILIP P. BARBOUR, Speaker
Kate Flournoy Edwards, 1911, 29½″ x 24½″
Purchased 1911 by H. Res. 163, 61st Congress

NEG. NO. 34305

JOHN BELL, Speaker
Willie Betty Newman, 30'' x 24½''
Signed l.r. W. B. Newman, 1911
Purchased 1911 by H. Res. 163, 61st Congress

NEG. NO. 34306

JAMES G. BLAINE, Speaker
Freeman Thorp, 29½" x 24"
Signed l.l. Thorp, 1905
Purchased through private contributions

44

NEG. NO. 34307

LINN BOYD, Speaker
Signed u.r. Stanley Middleton, 1911; 29½'' x 24½''
Purchased 1911 by H. Res. 163, 61st Congress

NEG. NO. 34308

Joseph W. Byrns, Speaker
Signed l.r. E. Sophonisba Hergesheimer, 1937 ©; 45″ x 35″
Purchased 1937 by Public No. 4, 75th Congress

46

NEG. NO. 34309

JOSEPH G. CANNON, Speaker
William T. Smedley, 55″ x 35″
Signed u.l. W. T. Smedley 1912
Purchased 1917 by Public No. 2, 65th Congress

NEG. NO. 34310

JOHN G. CARLISLE, Speaker
Ellen Day Hale, 1911, 41″ x 33″
Purchased 1911 by H. Res. 163, 61st Congress

NEG. NO. 34311

LANGDON CHEVES, Speaker
Signed l.l. Hal Morrison; 1912, 29½″ x 24½″
Purchased 1911 by H. Res. 163, 61st Congress

NEG. NO. 34312

CHAMP CLARK, Speaker
Signed l.l. Boris B. Gordon, 1919; 47½″ x 33½″
Purchased 1919 by Public No. 275, 65th Congress

50

NEG. NO. 34313

HENRY CLAY, Speaker
Giuseppe Fagnani, oval, 27½″ x 21½″
Signed center r. Fagnani, 1852
Gift of the artist, 1852
Accepted by Jt. Res. No. 13, 32nd Congress

NEG. NO. 34314

HOWELL COBB, Speaker
Signed u.r. Lucy M. Stanton; 1912, 29½″ x 24½″
Purchased 1911 by H. Res. 163, 61st Congress

NEG. NO. 34315

SCHUYLER COLFAX, Speaker
Freeman Thorp, 1911, 29½'' x 24''
Purchased 1911 by H. Res. 163, 61st Congress

NEG. NO. 34316

CHARLES F. CRISP, Speaker
Robert Hinckley, 41½″ x 31″
Purchased about 1894

NEG. NO. 34317

JOHN W. DAVIS, Speaker
Signed u.l. W. D. Murphy, N.Y., 1911; 29½″ x 24½″
Purchased 1911 by H. Res. 163, 61st Congress

NEG. NO. 34318

JONATHAN DAYTON, Speaker
Signed l.r. Henry Harrison, 1911; 29½″ x 24½″
Purchased 1911 by H. Res. 163, 61st Congress

NEG. NO. 34319

JOHN NANCE GARNER, Speaker
Signed l.l. Seymour M. Stone, 1939; 44½″ x 34½″
Acquired 1940 by H. Res. 374, 76th Congress

NEG. NO. 34320

FREDERICK H. GILLETT, Speaker
Edmund C. Tarbell, 41½″ x 31½″
Signed l.r. Tarbell, 1920
Purchased 1925 by P.L. 631, 68th Congress

NEG. NO. 34321

GALUSHA A. GROW, Speaker
Signed l.r. Wm. A. Greaves, 1891; 45″ x 33″
Gift of State of Pennsylvania, 1892
Accepted by H. Res. of January 21, 1892, 52nd Congress

NEG. NO. 34322

David B. Henderson, Speaker
Freeman Thorp, 29″ x 24″
Signed u.r. Thorp, 1903
Purchased 1913

NEG. NO. 34323

ROBERT M. T. HUNTER, Speaker
Richard N. Brooke, 1911, 31½'' x 26½''
Signed l.r. R. N. Brooke
Purchased 1911 by H. Res. 163, 61st Congress

NEG. NO. 34324

JOHN W. JONES, Speaker
James B. Sword, 29½″ x 24½″
Signed l.r. J. B. Sword, 1911
Purchased 1911 by H. Res. 163, 61st Congress

NEG. NO. 34325

J. WARREN KEIFER, Speaker
Signed l.r. Chas. A. Gray; 45½" x 35"
Purchased 1911 by H. Res. 163, 61st Congress

NEG. NO. 34326

MICHAEL KERR, Speaker
Signed l.l. Chas. A. Gray, 1911; 29½″ x 24½″
Purchased 1911 by H. Res. 163, 61st Congress

NEG. NO. 34327

NICHOLAS LONGWORTH, Speaker
Robert Doblhoff, 53″ x 35½″
Signed l.l. Doblhoff, 1930
Purchased 1930 by Public No. 519, 71st Congress

NEG. NO. 34328

NATHANIEL MACON, Speaker
Robert D. Gauley, 1911, after W. G. Randall, 29″ x 24″
Purchased 1911 by H. Res. 163, 61st Congress

NEG. NO. 34329

JOSEPH W. MARTIN, JR., Speaker
Signed l.l. Boris B. Gordon, 1959; 39½″ x 29½″
Purchased 1948 by P.L. 519, 80th Congress

NEG. NO. 34330

JOHN W. MCCORMACK, Speaker
Signed l.r. Victor Lallier, 1966 ©; 39½″ x 29½″
Purchased 1962 by P.L. 87–730, 87th Congress

NEG. NO. 34331

FREDERICK A. C. MUHLENBERG, Speaker
Samuel B. Waugh, after Joseph Wright, 48½″ x 36″
Signed l.r. Waugh, copy 1881
Gift of State of Pennsylvania, 1881
Accepted by H. Res. of February 26, 1881, 46th Congress

NEG. NO. 34332

JAMES L. ORR, Speaker
Esther Edmonds, 1911, 29½″ x 24½″
Signed l.r. Edmonds
Purchased 1911 by H. Res. 163, 61st Congress

NEG. NO. 34333

WILLIAM PENNINGTON, Speaker
Signed u.r. Jos. Lauber, 1911; 31½″ x 25″
Purchased 1911 by H. Res. 163, 61st Congress

NEG. NO. 39583

JAMES K. POLK, Speaker
Rebecca Polk, 1911, after G. P. A. Healy, 30½″ x 25″
Purchased 1911 by H. Res. 163, 61st Congress

NEG. NO. 34335

THEODORE M. POMEROY, Speaker
George L. Clough, 26½" x 21"
Purchased 1921 by H. Res. 389, 66th Congress

NEG. NO. 34336

HENRY T. RAINEY, Speaker
Signed l.l. Howard Chandler Christy, 1935; 56½'' x 38½''
Purchased 1935 by P.L. 200, 74th Congress

NEG. NO. 34337

SAMUEL J. RANDALL, Speaker
Signed l.l. Wm. A. Greaves, 1891; after C. A. Fassett, 35½″ x 28½″
Gift of State of Pennsylvania, 1892
Accepted by H. Res. of January 21, 1892, 52nd Congress

NEG. NO. 34338

Sam Rayburn, Speaker
Douglas Chandor, 46½″ x 39″
Signed l.l. Chandor, 1941
Purchased 1941 by P.L. 145, 77th Congress

76

NEG. NO. 34339

THOMAS B. REED, Speaker
Signed u.l. John S. Sargent, 1891; 31″ x 25″
Gift of Members of the 51st Congress, 1891

NEG. NO. 34340

THEODORE SEDGWICK, Speaker
Edgar Parker, after Gilbert Stuart, 29½″ x 24½″
Gift of State of Massachusetts, 1888
Accepted by H. Res. of January 19, 1888, 50th Congress

NEG. NO. 34341

ANDREW STEVENSON, Speaker
Spencer Baird Nichols, 1911, 31½″ x 26″
Signed u.r. S. B. N.
Purchased 1911 by H. Res. 163, 61st Congress

NEG. NO. 34342

JOHN W. TAYLOR, Speaker
Caroline L. O. Ransom, 31½″ x 25″
Purchased 1900

NEG. NO. 34343

JONATHAN TRUMBULL, Speaker
Harry Ives Thompson, 35½″ x 28″
Signed l.r. H. I. Thompson, 1880
Gift of State of Connecticut, 1880
Accepted by H. Res. of December 21, 1880, 46th Congress

81

NEG. NO. 39578

JOSEPH B. VARNUM, Speaker
Charles L. Elliott, 39½″ x 33½″
Gift of State of Massachusetts, 1888
Accepted by H. Res. of January 19, 1888, 50th Congress

NEG. NO. 34345

JOHN WHITE, Speaker
Signed l.l. Gerard Barry, copy, 1911; 29½'' x 24½''
Purchased 1911 by H. Res. 163, 61st Congress

NEG. NO. 39582

ROBERT C. WINTHROP, Speaker
Daniel Huntington, 57½″ x 37½″
Gift of Citizens of Massachusetts, 1882
Accepted by H. Res. of June 27, 1882, 47th Congress

# SPEAKERS OF THE HOUSE OF REPRESENTATIVES

### SEVEN SMALL PORTRAITS

A collection of seven small portraits hangs in the office of the Speaker of the House, room H–210. There are no records of their acquisition, but it is known that they were hanging in the private office of the Speaker prior to 1900. It is a tradition that these seven portraits were the incentive for the present collection in the Speaker's Lobby. With two exceptions, these small portraits are lithographs.

NEG. NO. 32240

JOHN BELL
Charles Fenderich, 1841 13″ x 9″

NEG. NO. 32241

LINN BOYD
Unknown lithographer, 13″ x 9″

NEG. NO. 32242

JONATHAN DAYTON
Pencil or watered ink, 15½″ x 13″

85

NEG. NO. 22880

JAMES P. BUCHANAN, Chairman 1933–1937
Signed 1.1. Seymour M. Stone, 1946; 39½″ x 29½″
H–218

NEG. NO. 22873

JOSEPH W. BYRNS, Chairman 1931–1933
George B. Matthews, 39½″ x 29½″
Signed l.r. G. B. Matthews 1933
H–217

NEG. NO. 34591

CLARENCE CANNON, Chairman 1941–46, 1949–52, 1955–64
Charles J. Fox, 29½″ x 24½″
Signed l.r. C J Fox
H–218

NEG. NO. 24098

JOSEPH G. CANNON, Chairman 1889–1891, 1895–1903
Freeman Thorp, 40″ x 31″
Signed l.l. Thorp, 1914
H–216

NEG. NO. 31587

HENRY L. DAWES, Chairman 1869–1871
Photograph
In storage

NEG. NO. 24036

JOHN J. FITZGERALD, Chairman 1911–1917
Signed u.r. Kenyon Cox, 1917; 25½″ x 20½″
H–217

NEG. NO. 24035

JAMES A. GARFIELD, Chairman 1871–1875
Signed l.r. C Adèle Fassett, 1891; 53½'' x 33½''
H–216

NEG. NO. 24034

JAMES W. GOOD, Chairman 1919–1921
Signed u.l. John C. Johansen, 1921; 39½″ x 35″
H–217

NEG. NO. 31590

FRANK HISCOCK, Chairman 1881–1883
Photograph
In storage

NEG. NO. 31586

WILLIAM S. HOLMAN, Chairman 1876–1877, 1891–1893
Engraving
In storage

NEG. NO. 22872

MARTIN B. MADDEN, Chairman, 1921–1928
Signed l.r. Underwood & Underwood, 1926; 39½″ x 29″
H–217

100

NEG. NO. 38587

George H. Mahon, Chairman 1964–
Charles J. Fox, 1974, 39½″ x 29½″
Signed l.r. C J Fox
H–216

NEG. NO. 31589

JOSEPH D. SAYERS, Chairman 1893–1895
Photograph
In storage

NEG. NO. 34507

SAMUEL J. RANDALL, Chairman 1875–1876,
   1883–1889
Kathryne C. Dimmitt, 1962, after C. A. Fassett,
   25'' x 19''
Signed l.l. K. C. Dimmitt
H–216

NEG. NO. 24032

J. SWAGAR SHERLEY, Chairman 1918–1919
Signed u.r. Chas. Sneed Williams; 30″ x 25″
H–217

NEG. NO. 24033

THADDEUS STEVENS, Chairman 1865–1868
Mathew Brady, photograph oil tinted, 24½″ x 18½″
H–216

NEG. NO. 34592

JOHN TABER, Chairman 1947–48, 1953–54
Frank de Bruin Valerius, 39¼″ x 29½″
Signed u.r. Valerius—Toronto—1960
H–218

NEG. NO. 22715

James A. Tawney, Chairman 1905–1911
Freeman Thorp, 42¾″ x 29½″
Signed l.l. Thorp, 1911
In storage

106

NEG. NO. 24097

EDWARD T. TAYLOR, Chairman 1937–1941
Signed l.r. John C. Johansen, 1939; 39½″ x 29½″
H–218

NEG. NO. 31585

ELIHU B. WASHBURNE, Chairman 1868–1869
Engraving
In storage

NEG. NO. 22876

WILLIAM R. WOOD, Chairman 1929–1931
George B. Matthews, 29½'' x 24½''
H–217

# ARCHITECTS OF THE CAPITOL

### EIGHT PORTRAITS

NEG. NO. 34282

WILLIAM THORNTON, 1793–94
George B. Matthews, after Gilbert Stuart, 29½″ x 24½″
Signed l.l. Copy by Matthews, 1930
Acquired through employment of the artist at the Capitol, 1931
SB–14

NEG. NO. 34283

BENJAMIN H. LATROBE, 1803–11, 1815–17
George B. Matthews, after C. W. Peale, 29½″ x 24½″
Signed l.l. Matthews
Acquired through employment of the artist at the Capitol, 1931
SB–14

NEG. NO. 34284

CHARLES BULFINCH, 1818–29
George B. Matthews, after 1842 drawing by Alvan Clark, 29½″ x 24½″
Signed l.r. Matthews
Acquired through employment of the artist at the Capitol, 1931
SB–14

NEG. NO. 34285

THOMAS U. WALTER, 1851–65
Francisco Pausas, 1925, after a Brady photograph, 30″ x 23½″
Signed l.r. F. Pausas
Gift of grandson Clark Walter, 1926
SB–14

NEG. NO. 34286

EDWARD CLARK, 1865–1902
Constantino Brumidi, 35½″ x 28½″
Gift of the Clark family, 1929
Accepted by the Joint Committee on the Library
SB–15

NEG. NO. 34287

Elliott Woods, 1902–23
George B. Matthews, 29½'' x 24½''
Acquired through employment of the artist at the Capitol, 1931
SB–15

NEG. NO. 34288

DAVID LYNN, 1923–54
Charles J. Fox, 1954, 29½'' x 24½''
Signed l.r. C. J. Fox
Purchased 1956 by P. L. 624, 84th Congress
SB–15

J. GEORGE STEWART, 1954–70
Charles J. Fox, 29½″ x 24½″
Signed l.r. C. J. Fox
Gift of the Stewart family, 1970
Accepted by the Joint Committee on the Library
SB–15

# PROMINENT INDIVIDUALS

ELEVEN PORTRAITS

NEG. NO. 32187

GUNNING BEDFORD, JR.
Charles Willson Peale, 34″ x 26″
Bequest of Henrietta Bedford, 1872
House wing, third floor, east corridor

Delegate to the Continental Congress from Delaware 1783–85; member of the Constitutional Convention at Philadelphia in 1787 and signer of the Constitution.

NEG. NO. 23104

CARLO FRANZONI
Pietro Bonanni, 19″ x 15″
Signed on reverse Bonani, pinxt 1818
Gift of Dr. Charles H. Franzoni, 1924
Accepted by the Joint Committee on the Library
HB–29

Sculptor, native of Carrara, Italy. Came to Washington, D.C. about 1816, died 1819. His chief works are the Car of History clock and the relief of Justice.

NEG. NO. 23135

JOSHUA R. GIDDINGS
Caroline L. Ormes Ransom, 39½″ x 31½″
Purchased 1867
In storage

A Representative from Ohio; served in Congress intermittently from 1838 to 1859.

NEG. NO. 24198

PATRICK HENRY
George B. Matthews, after Thomas Sully, 29½″ x 24½″
Signed l.l. G. Matthews
Acquired through employment of the artist at the Capitol, about 1900
Senate wing, second floor, main corridor

Delegate to the Continental Congress from Virginia 1774–76; American statesman and orator; Governor of Virginia.

NEG. NO. 24480

JOHN PAUL JONES
George B. Matthews, after C. W. Peale, 44″ x 32″
Purchased 1891
212 Richard Brevard Russell Office Building

American Naval Officer in the Revolutionary War; founder of the American Navy; flew the first American flag ever shown on a regular man-of-war. Died in France in the diplomatic service.

122

NEG. NO. 22733

GENERAL LAFAYETTE
Ary Scheffer, 92″ x 62″
Signed l.r. A. Scheffer 1823
Gift of the artist to the House of Representatives, 1824
House Chamber

French statesman and military officer; served as a volunteer under General Washington in the American Revolution.

NEG. NO. 24200

JAMES LATIMER
Clawson Shakespeare Hammitt, 35½″ x 28½″
Gift of Mary Latimer, 1916
Accepted by the Joint Committee on the Library
Senate wing, third floor, south corridor

　　Lieutenant Colonel in the Continental Army; presided over the Delaware Convention, the first State to ratify the Constitution; lawyer.

Hon: Henry Laurens,
Pres: of the American Congress.
(Painted 1781. while in the Tower.)

NEG. NO. 34000

HENRY LAURENS
Attributed to John Singleton Copley, 1781, 30″ x 25″
Purchased 1886
S-209

Delegate to the Continental Congress from South Carolina, served as its President 1777-78; Minister to Holland. While en route to his post he was captured and held prisoner in the Tower of London for fifteen months and was exchanged for Lord Cornwallis, 1781.

NEG. NO. 34616

JOHN MARSHALL
Richard N. Brooke, after W. D. Washington, 9′ x 5′2′′
Signed l.r. R. N. Brooke, Washington, 1880
Purchased 1881
House wing, third floor, west corridor

Chief Justice of the United States 1801–35; soldier in the Revolutionary War; Member of Congress from Virginia and Secretary of State.

126

Ætalis suæ 21. Aº. 1616.

Matoaks als Rebecka daughter to the mighty Prince
Powhatan Emperour of Attanoughkomouck als Virginia
converted and baptized in the Christian faith, and
Wife to the Worll Mr Tho: Rolff.

NEG. NO. 24315

POCAHONTAS
Unknown artist, copy from original, 30″ x 25″
Gift of Henry S. Wellcome, 1899
Accepted by S. Res. of February 28, 1899, 55th Congress
S–233

American Indian princess; reputed to have saved Captain John Smith from execution; married to John Rolfe.

NEG. NO. 30636

SAM RAYBURN
Signed l.r. Tom Lea, 1966; 59½″ x 39½″
Gift from Texas State Society, 1966
Accepted by House Office Building Commission, 1964
Rayburn House Office Building, east entrance

A Representative from Texas; Mr. Rayburn has the distinction of serving as Speaker of the House of Representatives longer than any other man.

# Paintings

Rotunda
Senate Wing
House Wing
Central Section
Richard Brevard Russell Office Building
House Office Buildings

# PAINTINGS IN THE ROTUNDA

### EIGHT PAINTINGS

NEG. NO. 34252

BAPTISM OF POCAHONTAS AT JAMESTOWN, VIRGINIA, 1613
John G. Chapman, 12' x 18'
Purchased; placed November 30, 1840

# BAPTISM OF POCAHONTAS

At Jamestown Va. 1613

1. Pocahontas
2. John Rolfe
3. Alexander Whiteaker
4. Sir Thomas Dale
5. Sister of Pocahontas

6. Nantequaus, brother of Pocahontas
7. Opechancanough
8. Opachisco, uncle of Pocahontas
9. Richard Wyffin

10. Standard bearer
11. Mr. and Mrs. Forrest, the lady being the first gentlewoman to arrive in the colony

12. Henry Spilman
13. John and Anne Laydon, the first persons married in the colony
14. The page

NEG. NO. 34253

DECLARATION OF INDEPENDENCE IN CONGRESS, AT THE INDEPENDENCE HALL, PHILADELPHIA, JULY 4TH, 1776
John Trumbull, 12' x 18'
Purchased March 4, 1819

# DECLARATION OF INDEPENDENCE

## In Congress, at the Independence Hall, Philadelphia, July 4th 1776.

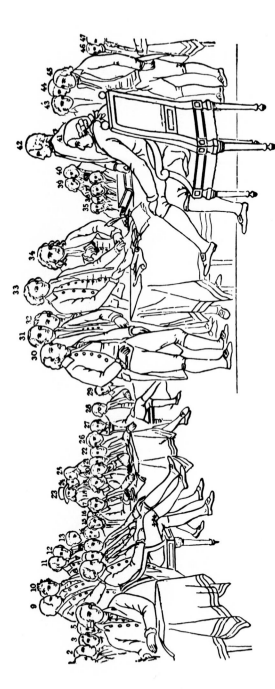

1. George Wythe, Virginia
2. William Whipple, New Hampshire
3. Josiah Bartlett, New Hampshire
4. Benjamin Harrison, Virginia
5. Thomas Lynch, South Carolina
6. Richard Henry Lee, Virginia
7. Samuel Adams, Massachusetts
*8. George Clinton, New York
9. William Paca, Maryland
10. Samuel Chase, Maryland
11. Lewis Morris, New York
12. William Floyd, New York

13. Arthur Middleton, South Carolina
14. Thomas Heyward, Jr., South Carolina
15. Charles Carroll, Maryland
16. George Walton, Georgia
17. Robert Morris, Pennsylvania
*18. Thomas Willing, Pennsylvania
19. Benjamin Rush, Pennsylvania
20. Elbridge Gerry, Massachusetts
21. Robert Treat Paine, Massachusetts
22. Abraham Clark, New Jersey
23. Stephen Hopkins, Rhode Island
24. William Ellery, Rhode Island

25. George Clymer, Pennsylvania
26. William Hooper, North Carolina
27. Joseph Hewes, North Carolina
28. James Willson, Pennsylvania
29. Francis Hopkinson, New Jersey
30. John Adams, Massachusetts
31. Roger Sherman, Connecticut
*32. Robert R. Livingston, New York
33. Thomas Jefferson, Virginia
34. Benjamin Franklin, Pennsylvania
35. Richard Stockton, New Jersey
36. Francis Lewis, New York

37. John Witherspoon, New Jersey
38. Samuel Huntington, Connecticut
39. William Williams, Connecticut
40. Oliver Wolcott, Connecticut
41. John Hancock, Massachusetts
*42. Charles Thomson, Secretary, Pennsylvania
43. George Read, Delaware
*44. John Dickinson, Pennsylvania
45. Edward Rutledge, South Carolina
46. Thomas McKean, Delaware
47. Philip Livingston, New York

There were 56 signers of the Declaration of Independence. The painting portrays only 47. The 5 men whose names are starred were not signers. The portraits of the following 14 signers do not appear in the painting.

Matthew Thornton, New Hampshire
John Hart, New Jersey
John Morton, Pennsylvania
James Smith, Pennsylvania

George Taylor, Pennsylvania
George Ross, Pennsylvania
Caesar Rodney, Delaware
Thomas Stone, Maryland

Thomas Nelson, Jr., Virginia
Francis Lightfoot Lee, Virginia
Carter Braxton, Virginia
John Penn, North Carolina

Button Gwinnett, Georgia
Lyman Hall, Georgia

133

NEG. NO. 34254

Discovery of the Mississippi by De Soto A.D. 1541
William H. Powell, 12′ x 18′
Signed l.r. W. H. Powell, 1853
Purchased; placed February 16, 1855

# DE SOTO'S DISCOVERY OF THE MISSISSIPPI
## A.D. 1541

1. De Soto
2. Moorish servant
3. Confessor
4. Spanish cavalier

5. Artillerymen
6. Company of men planting a cross
7. Ecclesiastic bearing the censer

8. Priest blessing the cross
9. Soldier dressing his wounded leg
10. Camp chest with arms and helmets

11. Standard bearers and helmeted men
12. Two Indian maidens
13. Indian chiefs bearing the pipe of peace

NEG. NO. 34255

EMBARKATION OF THE PILGRIMS AT DELFT HAVEN, HOLLAND, JULY 22ND, 1620
Signed ll. Robt. W. Weir, 1843; 12′ x 18′
Purchased; placed December 21, 1843

136

# EMBARKATION OF THE PILGRIMS
## At Delft Haven, Holland, July 22nd 1620.

1. Mr. Robinson, pastor of the congregation
2. Elder William Brewster
3. Mrs. Brewster and sick child
4. Governor Carver
5. William Bradford
6. Mr. and Mrs. White
7. Mr. and Mrs. Winslow
8. Mr. and Mrs. Fuller
9. Miles Standish and his wife Rose
10. Mrs. Bradford; she fell overboard the day the vessel came to anchor
11. Mrs. Carver and child
12. Captain Reynolds and sailor
13. Boy belonging to Carver and family
14. Boy in charge of Mr. Winslow
15. Boy belonging to Mrs. Winslow's family
16. A nurse and child

NEG. NO. 34256

GENERAL GEORGE WASHINGTON RESIGNING HIS COMMISSION TO CONGRESS AS COMMANDER IN CHIEF OF THE ARMY
AT ANNAPOLIS, MARYLAND, DECEMBER 23D, 1783
John Trumbull, 12' x 18'
Purchased December 24, 1824

138

# GEN. WASHINGTON RESIGNING HIS COMMISSION
## to Congress at Annapolis Md. Decemb. 23ᵈ 1783

1. Thomas Mifflin, Pennsylvania, President
   Delegate
2. Charles Thompson, Pennsylvania
   Secretary
3. Elbridge Gerry, Massachusetts
   Delegate
4. Hugh Williamson, North Carolina
   Delegate
5. Samuel Osgood, Massachusetts
   Delegate
6. Eleazer McComb, Delaware
   Delegate
7. George Partridge, Massachusetts
   Delegate
8. Edward Lloyd, Maryland
   Delegate
9. Richard D. Spaight, North Carolina
   Delegate
10. Benjamin Hawkins, North Carolina
    Delegate
11. Abiel Foster, New Hampshire
    Delegate
12. Thomas Jefferson, Virginia
    Delegate
13. Arthur Lee, Virginia
    Delegate
14. David Howell, Rhode Island
    Delegate
15. James Monroe, Virginia
    Delegate
16. Jacob Read, South Carolina
    Delegate
17. James Madison, Virginia
    Spectator
18. William Ellery, Rhode Island
    Delegate
19. J. Townley Chase, Maryland
    Delegate
20. Samuel Hardy, Virginia
    Delegate
21. Charles Morris, Pennsylvania
    Delegate
22. General Washington
23. Col. Benjamin Walker
    Aide-de-camp
24. Col. David Humphreys
    Aide-de-camp
25. General Smallwood, Maryland
    Spectator
26. Gen. Otho Holland Williams, Maryland
    Spectator
27. Col. Samuel Smith, Maryland
    Spectator
28. Col. John E. Howard, Maryland
    Spectator
29. Charles Carroll and two daughters,
    Maryland
30. Mrs. Washington and her three grand-
    children
31. Daniel of St. Thomas Jenifer, Maryland
    Spectator

139

NEG. NO. 34257

LANDING OF COLUMBUS AT THE ISLAND OF GUANAHANI, WEST INDIES, OCTOBER 12TH, 1492
John Vanderlyn, 12' x 18'
Purchased; placed January 15, 1847

140

# LANDING OF COLUMBUS

## At the Island of Guanahani, West-Indies. October 12th 1492.

1. Columbus
2. Martin Alonzo Pinzon
3. Vincent Yannez Pinzon
4. Rodrigo des Escobedo or Escobar, notary of the armament
5. Roderigo Sanchez, inspector of armament
6. Mutineer in a suppliant attitude
7. Alonzo de Ojeda
8. Cabin boy
9. Soldier
10. Sailor
11. Friar bearing a crucifix

NEG. NO. 34258

Surrender of General Burgoyne at Saratoga, New York, October 17th, 1777
John Trumbull, 12′ x 18′
Purchased May 1, 1822

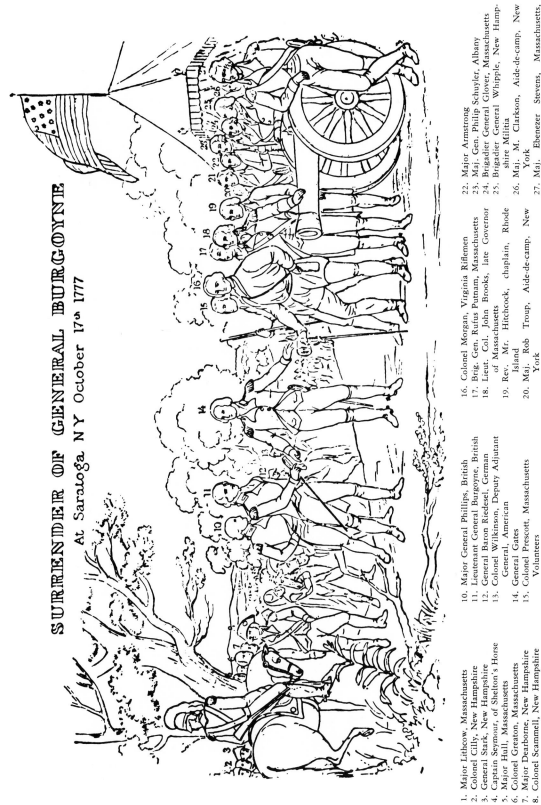

# SURRENDER OF GENERAL BURGOYNE
## At Saratoga N.Y. October 17ᵗʰ 1777

1. Major Lithcow, Massachusetts
2. Colonel Cilly, New Hampshire
3. General Stark, New Hampshire
4. Captain Seymour, of Shelton's Horse
5. Major Hull, Massachusetts
6. Colonel Greaton, Massachusetts
7. Major Dearborne, New Hampshire
8. Colonel Scammell, New Hampshire
9. Colonel Lewis, Quartermaster General, New Hampshire
10. Major General Phillips, British
11. Lieutenant General Burgoyne, British
12. General Baron Riedesel, German
13. Colonel Wilkinson, Deputy Adjutant General, American
14. General Gates
15. Colonel Prescott, Massachusetts Volunteers
16. Colonel Morgan, Virginia Riflemen
17. Brig. Gen. Rufus Putnam, Massachusetts
18. Lieut. Col. John Brooks, late Governor of Massachusetts
19. Rev. Mr. Hitchcock, chaplain, Rhode Island
20. Maj. Rob Troup, Aide-de-camp, New York
21. Major Haskell
22. Major Armstrong
23. Maj. Gen. Philip Schuyler, Albany
24. Brigadier General Glover, Massachusetts
25. Brigadier General Whipple, New Hampshire Militia
26. Maj. M. Clarkson, Aide-de-camp, New York
27. Maj. Ebenezer Stevens, Massachusetts, commanding the artillery

143

NEG. NO. 34259

SURRENDER OF LORD CORNWALLIS AT YORKTOWN, VIRGINIA, OCTOBER 19TH, 1781
John Trumbull, 12' x 18'
Purchased November 13, 1820

144

# SURRENDER OF LORD CORNWALLIS

At Yorktown Va. October 19th 1781.

The portraits of the French Officers were obtained in Paris 1787 and painted by Trumbull from life, of Mr. Jefferson then Minister to France from the United States.

1. Count Deuxponts
   Colonel of French Infantry
2. Duke de Laval Montmorency
   Colonel of French Infantry
3. Count Custine
   Colonel of French Infantry
4. Duke de Lauzun
   Colonel of French Cavalry
5. General Choizy
6. Viscount Viomenil
7. Marquis de St. Simon
8. Count Fersen
   Aide-de-camp of Count Rochambeau
9. Count Charles Damas
   Aide-de-camp of Count Rochambeau
10. Marquis Chastellux
11. Baron Viomenil
12. Count de Barras
    Admiral
13. Count de Grasse
    Admiral
14. Count Rochambeau
    General en Chef des Francais
15. General Lincoln
16. E. Stevens
    Colonel of American Artillery
17. General Washington.
    Commander in Chief
18. Thomas Nelson
    Governor of Virginia
19. Marquis Lafayette
20. Baron Steuben
21. Colonel Cobb
    Aide-de-camp to General Washington
22. Colonel Trumbull
    Secretary to General Washington
23. Maj. Gen. James Clinton, New York
24. General Gist, Maryland
25. Gen. Anthony Wayne, Pennsylvania
26. General Hand, Pennsylvania
    Adjutant General
27. Gen. Peter Muhlenberg, Pennsylvania
28. Maj. Gen. Henry Knox
    Commander of Artillery
29. Lieut. Col. E. Huntington
    Acting Aide-de-camp of General Lincoln
30. Col. Timothy Pickering
    Quartermaster General
31. Col. Alexander Hamilton
    commanding Light Infantry
32. Col. John Laurens, South Carolina
33. Col. Walter Stuart, Philadelphia
34. Col. Nicholas Fish, New York

145

## PAINTINGS IN THE SENATE WING

TWELVE PAINTINGS

BATTLE OF CHAPULTEPEC (STORMING OF CHAPULTEPEC)
James Walker, 17'6'' x 7'9½''
Purchased 1857–1862
In storage

NEG. NO. 34618

BATTLE OF FORT MOULTRIE
John Blake White, 1815, 32'' x 50''
Gift of Dr. Octavius A. White, 1901
Accepted by the Joint Committee on the Library
Senate wing, third floor, south corridor

147

NEG. NO. 34619

BATTLE OF LAKE ERIE
William H. Powell, 20′ x 30′
Signed 1.1 W. H. Powell. 1873
Purchased 1865
Senate wing, east staircase

148

NEG. NO. 34620

ELECTORAL COMMISSION OF 1877 (FLORIDA CASE)
Cornelia A. Fassett, 61½'' x 75''
Signed l.r. C. A. Fassett, 1879
Purchased 1886
Senate wing, third floor, east corridor

# THE ELECTORAL COMMISSION OF 1877 (THE FLORIDA CASE)

## IN THE GALLERY.

### (The Press.)

1. W. H. ROBERTS, New Orleans Times.
2. JOHN M. CARSON, New York Times.
3. BEN. PERLEY POORE, Boston Journal
4. GEORGE W. ADAMS, New York World.
5. T. C. CRAWFORD, Chicago Times.
6. A. M. GIBSON, New York Sun.
7. W. SCOTT SMITH, New York Evening Post.
8. C. W. FITCH, Pittsburgh Chronicle.
9. H. V. BOYNTON, Cincinnati Gazette.
10. WILSON J. VANCE, Cincinnati Commercial.
11. Mrs. JANE G. SWISSHELM.
12. L. A. GOBRIGHT, N.Y. Associated Press.
13. Mrs. S. J. LIPPINCOTT, ("Grace Greenwood,") N.Y. Times.
14. Miss AUSTINE SNEAD, ("Miss Grundy,") N.Y. Graphic.
15. Miss EMMA JANES, Toledo Blade, &c.
16. Mrs. MARY E. NEALY, Home Journal.
17. Mrs. M. D. LINCOLN, ("Bessie Beech,") Cleveland Plain-dealer.
18. Miss SALLIE WOODBURY, ("Ruby Wood,") National Union.
19. Mrs. FANNIE B. WARD, New Orleans Picayune.
20. Mrs. ADELE M. GARRIGUES, Courier East Saginaw, Mich.
21. W. M. OLIN, Boston Advertiser.
22. W. O. FISHBACK, St. Louis Republican.
23. DeB. R. KEIM, Philadelphia Press.
24. CROSBY S. NOYES, Ed. Evening Star, Washington, D.C.
25. JAMES R. YOUNG, Philadelphia Evening Star.
26. W. E. CURTIS, Chicago Inter-Ocean.
27. E. B. WIGHT, Chicago Tribune.
28. CHARLES LUTHER, Boston Post.
29. CHARLES NORDHOFF, New York Herald.
30. CLIFFORD WARDEN, Pitts-burgh Telegraph.
31. F. A. RICHARDSON, Baltimore Sun.
32. E. V. SMALLEY, New York Tribune.
33. L. Q. WASHINGTON, Louisville Courier-Journal.
34. Mrs. E. S. CROMWELL, Chicago Herald.
35. Miss NELLIE S. STOWELL, Kansas City Journal.
36. Mrs. FAYETTA C. SNEAD, ("Fay,") Louisville Courier-Journal.
37. Mrs. A. ROWLAND, Oxford (Pa.) Press.
38. FRANK HATTON, Ed. Burling-ton Hawkeye.
39. Ed. STODDARD, JOHNSON, Frankfort Yeoman.
40. A. C. BUELL, The Capital, Washington.
41. Mrs. A. D. JOHNSTON, Rochester Democrat and Chronicle.
42. Miss MARY E. MANN, Troy Daily Times.
43. CHARLES L. FLANAGAN, Philadelphia North American.
44. Mrs. ELVIRA BLISS SHELDON, ("Aunt True,") Grand Rapids Eagle.
45. W. HARRY CLARKE, National Associated Press.
46. I. N. BURRITT, Ed. Washington Herald.
47. C. CATHCART TAYLOR, Philadelphia Times.
48. WM. P. COPELAND, New York Commercial Bulletin.
49. E. F. WATERS, Prop. Boston Advertiser.
50. J. EDWARDS CLARKE, New York Mail.
51. JNO. C. BURCH, Ed. Nashville American.
52. Mr. GODDARD, Ed. Boston Advertiser.
53. HOWARD CARROL, New York Times.
54. S. H. KAUFFMANN, Evening Star.
55. WM. C. MAC BRIDE, Cincinnati Enquirer.
56. Z. L. WHITE, New York Tribune.
57. EDWIN FLEMING, N.Y. Journal of Commerce.
58. L. W. KENNEDY, Daily Chronicle, Washington, D.C.
59. M. DEE, Detroit Evening News.
60. GEORGE DOUGLAS, Washing-ton Capital.
61. Mr. PARR, Pittsburgh Post.
62. Mrs. G. W. THOMSON, Journal.

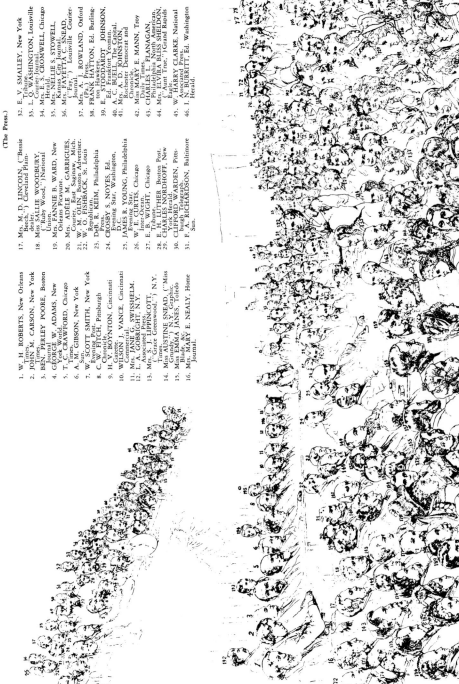

Copyright 1878 by Mrs S M Fassett

## THE COMMISSIONERS.

United States Senators.
1. Ohio.
2. Delaware.
3. New Jersey.
4. Indiana.
5. Vermont.

Associate Justices of the Supreme Court of the United States.
6. Pennsylvania.
7. Iowa. — *Saml. F. Miller*
8. Maine. — President of the Commission
9. California.
10. New Jersey.

Members of the House of Representatives.
11. Ohio.
12. Virginia.
13. Massachusetts.
14. Ohio.
15. Massachusetts.

16. U.S. Sen. — New York.

Substitute for Allen G. Thurman during his illness.

17. WILLIAM WINDOM, Senator, Minnesota.
18. W. W. CORCORAN.
19. JOHN J. INGALLS, Senator, Kansas.
20. J. C. S. BLACKBURN, Member of Congress, Kentucky.
21. JOHN H. REAGAN, Member of Congress, Texas.
22. B. E. CATTIN, Assistant Secretary Electoral Com.
23. GEORGE A. HOWARD, Assistant Secretary Electoral Com.
24. JAMES H. McKENNEY, Secretary Electoral Commission.
25. JOHN SHERMAN, Senator, Ohio.
26. SAMUEL SHELLABARGER, Counsel for Hayes.
27. WILLIAM F. COOPER, Page to Electoral Commission.
28. D. F. MURPHY, Stenographer Electoral Commission.
29. GEORGE W. McCRARY, M. C., Ia., and counsel for Hayes.
30. MORRISON R. WAITE, Chief Justice, U.S.S.C.
31. JOHN G. THOMPSON, Sergeant-at-Arms, H.R.
32. JOHN J. NICOLAY, Marshall, U.S.S.C.
33. W. H. REARDON, Marshall, Electoral Commission.
34. E. P. CORVAIZIER, Messenger, U.S. Senate.
35. MRS. Z. CHANDLER.
36. MISS G. A. BOUTWELL.
37. JOHN R. FRENCH, Sergeant-at-Arms, U.S. Senate.
38. MISS G. F. TUCKER.
39. MRS. CHARLES E. HOOKER.
40. MISS CAROLINE BRADLEY.
41.
42. MISS LIDA MILLER.
43. MISS JULIA D. STRONG.
44. PROF. JOSEPH HENRY, Smithsonian Institution.
45. CHARLES G. WILLIAMS, Member of Congress, Wisconsin.
46. MRS. S. VIRGINIA FIELD.
47. MRS. MARY A. MATTHEWS.
48. MRS. RUTH A. HOAR.
49. MRS. CHAPMAN COLEMAN.
50. HAMILTON FISH, Secretary of State.
51. MRS. JULIA K. FISH.
52. MRS. MYRA CLARK GAINES.
53. MRS. JULIA G. TYLER, (Widow of Ex-President Tyler.)
54. MRS. I. V. SWEARINGEN.
55. MRS. VIRGINIA M. WILSON.
56. MRS. RACHAEL H. STRONG.
57. CHARLES GORDON.
58. MRS. IMOGENE R. MORRILL.
59. MRS. JEAN M. LANDER.
60. MISS KATHERINE LEE BAYARD.
61. JOHN J. PATTERSON, Senator, South Carolina.
62. MRS. CATHERINE HARDENBERGH.
63. JOHN H. FLAGG, Legislative Clerk, U.S. Senate.
64. JOHN HITZ, Consul General of Switzerland.
65. CHARLES PAGE BRYAN.
66. GEORGE M. ADAMS, Clerk, House of Representatives.
67. HORATIO KING.
68. S. W. DORSEY, Senator, Arkansas.
69. M. B. BRADY.
70. AMBROSE E. BURNSIDE, Senator, Rhode Island.
71. GEORGE C. GORHAM, Secretary, U.S. Senate.
72. SAMUEL J. RANDALL, Speaker, House of Representatives.
73. F. M. COCKRELL, Senator, Missouri.
74. J. PROCTOR KNOTT, Member of Congress, Kentucky.
75. JOHN B. CLARK, Jr., Member of Congress, Missouri.
76. H. B. ANTHONY, Senator, Rhode Island.
77. BAINBRIDGE WADLEIGH, Senator, New Hampshire.
78. BENJAMIN H. HILL, Senator, Georgia.
79. FERNANDO WOOD, Member of Congress, New York.
80. A. C. HARMER, Member of Congress, Pa.
81. ANNANIAS HERBERT, Messenger, U.S. Supreme Court.
82. G. A. CLARK, Doorkeeper, U.S. Supreme Court.
83. AUGUSTUS W. CUTLER, Member of Congress, New Jersey.
84. A. R. SHEPHERD.
85. S. L. PHELPS, Commissioner, District of Columbia.
86. J. W. POWELL, United States Survey.
87. S. A. HURLBUT, M. C., Ill., and counsel for Hayes.
88. JOHN A. KASSON, M. C., Ia., and counsel for Hayes.
89. GEORGE W. CHILDS.
90. JAMES L. ANDEM, Reporter for N.Y. Asso. Press.
91. STANLEY MATTHEWS, Counsel for Hayes.
92. MRS. J. A. GARFIELD.
93. GEORGE M. ROBESON, Secretary of Navy.
94. ALPHONSO M. TAFT, Secretary of War.
95. BEIVA M. LOCKWOOD.
96. GEORGE S. BOUTWELL, Senator, Massachusetts.
97. AARON SARGENT, Senator, California.
98. DR. PETER PARKER.
99. JAMES O. WOODRUFF, Scientific Expedition.
100. EUGENE HALE, Member of Congress, Maine.
101. CHARLES FOSTER, Member of Congress, Ohio.
102. JOHN H. MITCHELL, Senator, Oregon.
103. W. P. LYNDE, Member of Congress, Wisconsin.
104. JOHN D. CATKINS, Member of Congress, Tennessee.
105. A. A. HARDENBERGH, Member of Congress, New Jersey.
106. THOMAS EWING, Member of Congress, Ohio.
107. WILLIAM E. CHANDLER, Counsel for Hayes.
108. JAMES P. ROOT, Counsel for Hayes.
109. JAMES N. TYNER, Postmaster General.
110. WILLIAM LAWRENCE, M. C., Ohio, counsel for Hayes.
111. D. T. CORBIN.
112. C. D. DRAKE, Chief Justice, U.S. C. of Claims.
113. CHARLES W. JONES, Senator, Florida.
114. P. PHILLIPS.
115. SAUNDERS W. JOHNSTON.
116. N. P. BANKS, Member of Congress, Massachusetts.
117. J. G. CANNON, Member of Congress, Illinois.
118. FLORA FASSETT.
119. ELIZABETH B. JOHNSTON.
120. W. A. J. SPARKS, Member of Congress, Illinois.
121. FREDERICK DOUGLASS.
122. WILLIAM M. EVARTS, Counsel for Hayes.
123. EDWIN W. STOUGHTON, Counsel for Hayes.
124. ZACHARIAH CHANDLER, Secretary of the Interior.
125. ABRAM S. HEWITT, Member of Congress, New York.
126. AMERICUS V. RICE, Member of Congress, Ohio.
127. MRS. CELIA S. SHERMAN.
128. MRS. JENNIE B. BRYAN.
129. MRS. SUSAN M. EDMUNDS.
130. MRS. E. V. MILLER.
131. WILLIAM D. KELLEY, Member of Congress, Pennsylvania.
132. MRS. MARY CLEMMER.
133. CHARLES O'CONOR, Counsel for Tilden.
134. RICHARD T. MERRICK, Counsel for Tilden.
135. GEORGE A. JENKS, M. C., Pa., and counsel for Tilden.
136. W. H. FORNEY, Member of Congress, Alabama.
137. J. RANDOLPH TUCKER, M. C., Va., and counsel for Tilden.
138. TIMOTHY O. HOWE, Sen., Wis., and counsel for Hayes.
139. HENRY WATTERSON, Member of Congress, Kentucky.
140. MRS. ELLEN F. WINDOM.
141. THOMAS B. BRYAN.
142. HIRAM P. BELL, Member of Congress, Georgia.
143. L. Q. C. LAMAR, Member of Congress, Mississippi.
144. HANNIBAL HAMLIN, Senator, Maine.
145. GEORGE BANCROFT, Historian.
146. JUSTIN S. MORRILL, Senator, Vermont.
147. JOHN A. CAMPBELL, Counsel for Tilden.
148. ROSCOE CONKLING, Senator, New York.
149. MONTGOMERY BLAIR, Counsel for Tilden.
150. MATT W. RANSOM, Senator, North Carolina.
151. DAVID DUDLEY FIELD, M. C., N.Y., counsel for Tilden.
152. WILLIAM C. WHITNEY, Counsel for Tilden.
153. THOMAS W. FERRY, President pro Tempore, U.S. Senate.
154. JAMES H. BLOUNT, Member of Congress, Georgia.
155. J. D. CAMERON, Senator, Pennsylvania.
156. MARTIN I. TOWNSEND, Member of Congress, New York.
157. WILLIAM M. SPRINGER, Member of Congress, Illinois.
158. LYMAN TRUMBULL, Counsel for Tilden.
159. MATT H. CARPENTER, Counsel for Tilden.
160. JEREMIAH S. BLACK, Counsel for Tilden.
161. GEORGE HOADLY, Counsel for Tilden.
162. ASHABEL GREEN, Counsel for Tilden.
163. MATTHEW G. EMERY.
164. ALEX. PORTER MORSE, Counsel for Tilden.
165. H. B. BANNING, Member of Congress, Ohio.
166. MRS. NANNIE MERRICK.
167. BLANCHE K. BRUCE, Senator, Mississippi.
168. HENRY W. BLAIR, Member of Congress, New Hampshire.
169. MISS CELIA V. RICE.
170. MRS. CHRISTINE TYNER.
171. SIR EDWARD THORNTON, British Minister.
172. HIESTER CLYMER, Member of Congress, Pennsylvania.
173. MRS. LAURA H. TUCKER.
174. MRS. FANNIE H. GORDON.
175. JOHN B. GORDON, Senator, Georgia.
176. JOHN A. LOGAN, Senator, Illinois.
177. S. S. COX, Member of Congress, New York.
178. MARY F. WAITE.
179. MRS. HELEN M. DORSEY.
180. THOMAS SWAN, Member of Congress, Maryland.
181. MRS. MARY CAMERON.
182. MRS. C. ADELE FASSETT.
183. MRS. MARY A. RICE.
184. JAMES G. BLAINE, Senator, Maine.
185. MRS. SALLIE B. KNOTT.
186. CARLILE P. PATTERSON, Superintendent U.S. Coast Survey.
187. MRS. C. P. PATTERSON.
188. MRS. MARY M. GIBSON.
189. W. B. ALLISON, Senator, Iowa.
190. RANDALL LEE GIBSON, Member of Congress, Louisiana.
191. MRS. LILLIE E. WILLIS.
192. CHARLES W. HOFFMAN, Librarian of Law Library, U.S.S.C.
193. C. H. McCALL, Page, Supreme Court U.S.
194. ROBERT BROWN, Page, Supreme Court U.S.
195. FRED W. MATTESON, Page, Supreme Court U.S.
196. H. J. LAUCK, Messenger, Electoral Commission.

NEG. NO. 34621

First Reading of the Emancipation Proclamation
Francis Bicknell Carpenter, 1864, 9′ x 14′ 6″
Gift of Mrs. Elizabeth Thompson, 1878
Accepted by Public Res. 6, 45th Congress
Senate wing, west staircase

152

# THE FIRST READING OF THE EMANCIPATION PROCLAMATION

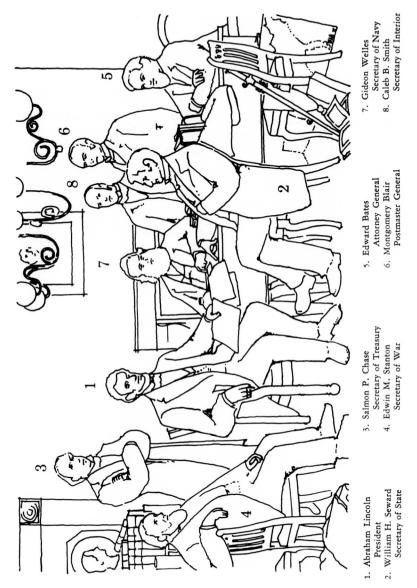

1. Abraham Lincoln
   President
2. William H. Seward
   Secretary of State

3. Salmon P. Chase
   Secretary of Treasury
4. Edwin M. Stanton
   Secretary of War

5. Edward Bates
   Attorney General
6. Montgomery Blair
   Postmaster General

7. Gideon Welles
   Secretary of Navy
8. Caleb B. Smith
   Secretary of Interior

NEG. NO. 34622

GENERAL MARION INVITING A BRITISH OFFICER TO SHARE HIS MEAL
John Blake White, about 1810–1815, 24½″ x 29½″
Gift of Dr. Octavius A. White, 1899
Accepted by Senate Res. 510, 55th Congress
Senate wing, third floor, south corridor

154

NEG. NO. 34623

Leiv Eiriksson Discovers America, A.D. 1000
Per Krohg, after Christian Krohg, 5'5½'' x 8'4''
Signed l.r. efter C. Krohg 1893, ved P. Krohg 1936
Gift of Norwegian friends of America through
 Dr. Alf Bjercke of Oslo, Norway, 1936
Accepted by Public Res. 78, 74th Congress
Senate wing, third floor, east corridor

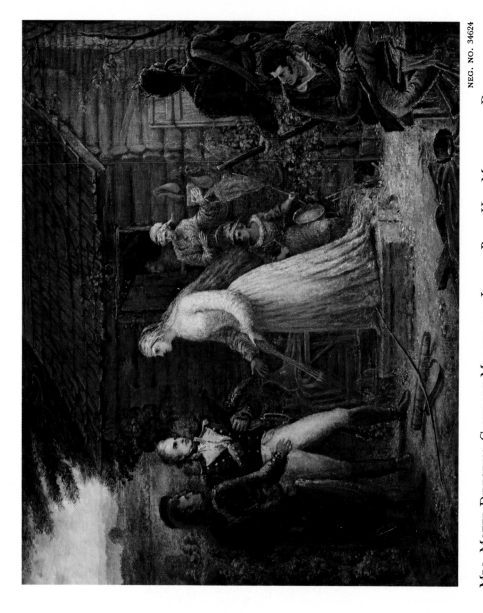

NEG. NO. 34624

Mrs. Motte Directing Generals Marion and Lee to Burn Her Mansion to Dislodge the British

John Blake White, about 1810–1815, 24½″ x 29½″
Gift of Dr. Octavius A. White, 1899
Accepted by Senate Res. 510, 55th Congress
Senate wing, third floor, south corridor

NEG. NO. 24475

Niagara Falls in Winter
Regis Gignoux, 1848, 52″ x 36″
Signed l.r. R. Gignoux
Gift of Mrs. Charles Carroll of Doughoregan Manor, Maryland
Accepted by the Joint Committee on the Library, 1901
Senate wing, third floor, south corridor

157

NEG. NO. 34626

RECALL OF COLUMBUS
Augustus G. Heaton, 51″ x 91″
Signed l.r. Copyright 1891 by A. G. Heaton, 1882
Purchased 1883

Senate wing, third floor, east corridor

NEG. NO. 34627

SERGEANTS JASPER AND NEWTON RESCUING AMERICAN PRISONERS FROM THE BRITISH
John Blake White, about 1810–1815, 24½″ x 29½″
Gift of Dr. Octavius A. White, 1899
Accepted by Senate Res. 510, 55th Congress
Senate wing, third floor, south corridor

WE (LINDBERGH'S FLIGHT)
Einar Kverne, 1927, 36″ x 50″
Gift of Robert W. Woodruff, 1928
Accepted by the Joint Committee on the Library
Location unknown. No Photograph

# PAINTINGS IN THE HOUSE WING

### FIVE PAINTINGS

NEG. NO. 34628

DISCOVERY OF THE HUDSON RIVER
Albert Bierstadt, 6' x 10'
Signed l.r. A. Bierstadt
Purchased 1875
Members' private stairway, east corridor

NEG. NO. 34629

Entrance Into Monterey
Albert Bierstadt, 6′ x 10′
Signed l.r. A. Bierstadt
Purchased 1878
Members' private stairway, west corridor

161

NEG. NO. 34630

SCENE AT THE SIGNING OF THE CONSTITUTION OF THE UNITED STATES
Signed l.r. Howard Chandler Christy, Sail Loft, U.S. Navy Yard, Washington, D.C., April 1940; 20' x 30'
Purchased 1940 by Public Res. 11, 76th Congress
House wing, east stairway

# SCENE AT THE SIGNING OF THE CONSTITUTION OF THE UNITED STATES

1. Washington, George, Va.
2. Franklin, Benjamin, Pa.
3. Madison, James, Va.
4. Hamilton, Alexander, N.Y.
5. Morris, Gouverneur, Pa.
6. Morris, Robert, Pa.
7. Wilson, James, Pa.
8. Pinckney, Chas. Cotesworth, S.C.
9. Pinckney, Chas, S.C.
10. Rutledge, John, S.C.

11. Butler, Pierce, S.C.
12. Sherman, Roger, Conn.
13. Johnson, William Samuel, Conn.
14. McHenry, James, Md.
15. Read, George, Del.
16. Bassett, Richard, Del.
17. Spaight, Richard Dobbs, N.C.
18. Blount, William, N.C.
19. Williamson, Hugh, N.C.
20. Jenifer, Daniel of St. Thomas, Md.

21. King, Rufus, Mass.
22. Gorham, Nathaniel, Mass.
23. Dayton, Jonathan, N.J.
24. Carroll, Daniel, Md.
25. Few, William, Ga.
26. Baldwin, Abraham, Ga.
27. Langdon, John, N.H.
28. Gilman, Nicholas, N.H.
29. Livingston, William, N.J.
30. Paterson, William, N.J.

31. Mifflin, Thomas, Pa.
32. Clymer, George, Pa.
33. FitzSimons, Thomas, Pa.
34. Ingersoll, Jared, Pa.
35. Bedford, Gunning, Jr., Del.
36. Brearley, David, N.J.
37. Dickinson, John, Del.
38. Blair, John, Va.
39. Broom, Jacob, Del.
40. Jackson, William, Secretary

NEG. NO. 36853

UNITED STATES CAPITOL, East Front
Signed l.r. Paul N. Norton; 1971, watercolor, 28½″ x 21″
Gift of the U.S. Capitol Historical Society, 1971
Accepted by the Joint Committee on the Library
H–107

NEG. NO. 34631

WESTWARD THE COURSE OF EMPIRE TAKES ITS WAY
Signed l.l. Painted by Emanuel Leutze 1862; fresco, 20′ x 30′
Commissioned 1861
House wing, west stairway

# PAINTINGS IN THE CENTRAL SECTION

EIGHTEEN PAINTINGS

LANDING OF COLUMBUS IN SAN SALVADOR
Signed l.l. Boris Plenkovich N.A., 1966; 31½″ x 39″
Gift from the National Columbus Day Committee, 1966
Accepted by the Joint Committee on the Library
In storage. Not illustrated

Seventeen paintings of historic forts by Brigadier General Seth Eastman all hang in the center building, first floor, west corridor. General Eastman, working under special orders from the President, depicted the principal fortifications of the United States. The paintings were executed between 1870 and the time of his death in 1875. The date is given if it appears on the canvas.

This collection includes:

Fort Defiance, New Mexico (now Arizona)
Fort Delaware, Delaware
Fort Jefferson, Florida
Fort Knox, Maine
Fort Lafayette, New York
Fort Mackinac, Michigan
Fort Mifflin, Pennsylvania
Fort Rice, North Dakota
Fort Scammel and Fort Gorges, Maine

Fort Snelling, Minnesota
Fort Sumter, South Carolina (before the war)
Fort Sumter, South Carolina (after the bombardment)
Fort Sumter, South Carolina (after the war)
Fort Taylor, Florida
Fort Tompkins and Fort Wadsworth, New York
Fort Trumbull, Connecticut
Fort West Point, New York

NEG. NO. 24110

FORT DEFIANCE, New Mexico (now Arizona)
Seth Eastman, 21½″ x 31½″
Signed bottom l. center S. E., 1873
Center section, first floor, west corridor

NEG. NO. 24894

FORT DELAWARE, Delaware
Seth Eastman, 24½″ x 35½″
Signed l.l. S. E.
Center section, first floor, west corridor

168

NEG. NO. 24895

FORT JEFFERSON, Florida
Seth Eastman, 1875; 21½″ x 31½″
Center section, first floor, west corridor

169

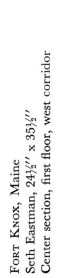

NEG. NO. 24896

FORT KNOX, Maine
Seth Eastman, 24½″ x 35½″
Center section, first floor, west corridor

170

NEG. NO. 24109

Fort Lafayette, New York
Seth Eastman, 24½″ x 35½″
Signed l.l. S. E.
Center section, first floor, west corridor

171

NEG. NO. 24897

FORT MACKINAC, Michigan
Seth Eastman, 24½″ x 35½″
Signed l.r. S. E., 1872
Center section, first floor, west corridor

172

NEG. NO. 24898

FORT MIFFLIN, Pennsylvania
Seth Eastman, 21½″ x 31½″
Signed l.l. S. Eastman, U.S.A., 1873
Center section, first floor, west corridor

173

NEG. NO. 24899

FORT RICE, North Dakota
Seth Eastman, 21½″ x 31½″
Signed l.r. S. E., 1873
Center section, first floor, west corridor

174

NEG. NO. 24900

FORT SCAMMEL AND FORT GORGES, Maine
Seth Eastman, 24½″ x 35½″
Signed l.r. S. E., 1872
Center section, first floor, west corridor

NEG. NO. 24901

FORT SNELLING, Minnesota
Seth Eastman, 24½'' x 35½''
Signed l.r. S. Eastman
Center section, first floor, west corridor

NEG. NO. 24106

FORT SUMTER, South Carolina (before the war)
Seth Eastman, 24½″ x 35½″
Signed l.r. S. E., 1871
Center section, first floor, west corridor

177

NEG. NO. 24107

FORT SUMTER, South Carolina (after the bombardment)
Seth Eastman, 24½'' x 35½''
Center section, first floor, west corridor

178

NEG. NO. 24108

FORT SUMTER, South Carolina (after the war)
Seth Eastman, 24½″ x 35½″
Signed bottom l. center S. E., 1870
Center section, first floor, west corridor

179

NEG. NO. 24902

FORT TAYLOR, Florida
Seth Eastman, 21½″ x 31½″
Center section, first floor, west corridor

NEG. NO. 24903

Fort Tompkins and Fort Wadsworth, New York
Seth Eastman, 24½″ x 35½″
Signed bottom l. center S. E.
Center section, first floor, west corridor

181

NEG. NO. 24105

FORT TRUMBULL, Connecticut
Seth Eastman, 24½″ x 35½″
Center section, first floor, west corridor

NEG. NO. 24104

FORT WEST POINT, NEW YORK
Seth Eastman, 24½″ x 35½″
Center section, first floor, west corridor

183

# PAINTING IN THE RICHARD BREVARD RUSSELL OFFICE BUILDING

## ONE PAINTING

BRIDES OF VENICE
J. H. Van Lerius, 8′ 1″ x 4′ ¾″
Gift of daughters of Mrs. Alice Pike Barney, 1934
Accepted by the Joint Committee on the Library
In storage. Not illustrated


# PAINTINGS IN THE HOUSE OFFICE BUILDINGS

## TEN PAINTINGS

Nine paintings of Indian scenes were executed by Brigadier General Seth Eastman between 1867 and 1869 under a special commission directing him to decorate the House Indian Affairs Committee room in the Capitol. In 1945 the committee (renamed Interior and Insular Affairs in 1951) moved to the Longworth House Office Building, room 1324, and the collection was hung there. The date of painting is given if it appears on the canvas.

The scenes represented are:

Buffalo Chase
Death Whoop
Dog Dance of the Dakotas
Feeding the Dead
Indian Council

Indian Mode of Traveling
Indian Woman Dressing a Deer Skin
Rice Gatherers
Spearing Fish in Winter

The marine painting, "Peace," represents the White Squadron as constituted in 1891, lying peacefully at anchor. This squadron was the nucleus of the modern U.S. Navy fleet.

NEG. NO. 34108

BUFFALO CHASE
Seth Eastman, 24″ x 31½″
Signed l.l. S. E. 1868
1324 Longworth House Office Building

185

NEG. NO. 34109

DEATH WHOOP
Seth Eastman, 38½″ x 28″
Signed l.r. S. E. 1868
1324 Longworth House Office Building

NEG. NO. 34110

DOG DANCE OF THE DAKOTAS
Seth Eastman, 31″ x 44″
Signed l.r. S. E. 1868
1324 Longworth House Office Building

187

NEG. NO. 34111

FEEDING THE DEAD
Seth Eastman, 24″ x 31½″
Signed l.r. S. E. 1868
1324 Longworth House Office Building

188

NEG. NO. 34112

INDIAN COUNCIL
Seth Eastman, 31″ x 44″
Signed l.r. S. E. 1868
1324 Longworᵗh House Office Building

189

NEG. NO. 34113

INDIAN MODE OF TRAVELING
Seth Eastman, 31″ x 44″
Signed l.l. S. E. 1869
1324 Longworth House Office Building

NEG. NO. 34114

INDIAN WOMAN DRESSING A DEER SKIN
Seth Eastman, 38½″ x 28″
1324 Longworth House Office Building

NEG. NO. 34115

RICE GATHERERS
Seth Eastman, 31½″ x 40½″
Signed l.l. S. E. 1867
1324 Longworth House Office Building

NEG. NO. 34116

SPEARING FISH IN WINTER
Seth Eastman, 31″ x 44″
1324 Longworth House Office Building

NEG. NO. 31549

PEACE
Signed l.l. Walter L. Dean; 6′ 3″ x 9′
Purchased 1928
311 Cannon House Office Building

# Busts

Presidents of the United States
Vice Presidents of the United States
Chief Justices of the United States
United States Senators
Speakers and Members of the House of Representatives
Prominent Individuals

# PRESIDENTS

TEN BUSTS

NEG. NO. 34634

GEORGE WASHINGTON
Signed r. side David d'Angers, 1828; bronze, 28″
Gift from the French Nation, 1905
Rotunda

This bronze is a 1905 casting from the original model made about 1828. It replaced the original marble bust that was destroyed by fire in 1851.

NEG. NO. 39189

GEORGE WASHINGTON
Antonio Capellano, 1827, sandstone, 29½″
Central section, first floor

Formerly part of the sandstone sculpture group, Fame and Peace Crowning Washington, that was on the East Central Portico. These figures were replaced in marble in 1960. See page 299.

NEG. NO. 29191

GEORGE WASHINGTON
Signed back of base D.A. Curtis © 1926; after William Rush, bronze, 26″
Bequest of Marie J. Niehaus, 1965
Accepted by the Joint Committee on the Library
EF-100, southeast niche

NEG. NO. 34635

GEORGE WASHINGTON
Of the Houdon school, marble, 32″
Gift of Mrs. James B. Drinker, 1966
Accepted by the Joint Committee on the Library
Niche adjacent to S-227

196

NEG. NO. 34171

JOHN QUINCY ADAMS
John Crookshanks King, marble, 20″
Signed l. side J. C. King, fecit 1845
Acquired 1849
H-235, Congresswomen's Suite

Mr. Adams died in this room in 1848, when it was the office of the Speaker of the House.

NEG. NO. 34632

ABRAHAM LINCOLN
Sarah Fisher Ames, marble, 35″
Purchased 1868
Senate wing, third floor, east corridor

NEG. NO. 34633

ABRAHAM LINCOLN
Signed l. side Gutzon Borglum, 1908; heroic
head, marble, 40″
Gift of Eugene Meyer, Jr., 1908
Accepted by the Joint Committee on the Library
Rotunda

NEG. NO. 229

ZACHARY TAYLOR
Unknown sculptor, marble, 25″
Purchased 1909
Senate wing, third floor, east corridor

NEG. NO. 30997

JAMES A. GARFIELD
Charles H. Niehaus, marble, 31″
Bequest of Marie J. Niehaus, 1966
Accepted by the Joint Committee on the Library
S–216, President's Room

NEG. NO. 25811

WILLIAM McKINLEY, JR.
Emma Cadwalader-Guild, bronze, 29″
Purchased 1903
S–216, President's Room

# VICE PRESIDENTS

### THIRTY-SEVEN BUSTS

Thirty-seven marble busts of Vice Presidents were acquired under authority of Senate resolutions of January 27, 1885, May 13, 1886, January 6, 1898 and March 28, 1947.

This collection includes all Vice Presidents from the first Vice President, John Adams, through Lyndon B. Johnson. Twenty of these busts are located in niches in the gallery walls of the Senate Chamber, 12 in the second floor corridors of the Senate wing adjacent to the Chamber, 1 in the Vice President's formal office, S-214, and 2 in the Senate Reception Room, S-213.

The busts of Richard M. Nixon and Lyndon B. Johnson have been completed. Because they have not been placed, photographs are not available.

The busts of Hubert H. Humphrey, Spiro T. Agnew, Gerald R. Ford and Nelson A. Rockefeller have not been executed.

| Vice President | State | Period of service | | Sculptor | Date of purchase |
|---|---|---|---|---|---|
| John Adams | Massachusetts | Apr. | 30, 1789–Mar. 3, 1797 | Daniel Chester French | 1890 |
| Thomas Jefferson | Virginia | Mar. | 4, 1797–Mar. 3, 1801 | Sir Moses Ezekiel | 1889 |
| Aaron Burr | New York | Mar. | 4, 1801–Mar. 3, 1805 | Jacques Jovenal | 1893 |
| George Clinton | New York | Mar. | 4, 1805–Apr. 20, 1812 | Vittorio A. Ciani | 1894 |
| Elbridge Gerry | Massachusetts | Mar. | 4, 1813–Nov. 23, 1814 | Herbert Adams | 1892 |
| Daniel D. Tompkins | New York | Mar. | 4, 1817–Mar. 3, 1825 | Charles H. Niehaus | 1891 |
| John C. Calhoun | South Carolina | Mar. | 4, 1825–Dec. 28, 1832 | Theodore A. Mills | 1896 |
| Martin Van Buren | New York | Mar. | 4, 1833–Mar. 3, 1837 | U. S. J. Dunbar | 1894 |
| Richard M. Johnson | Kentucky | Mar. | 4, 1837–Mar. 3, 1841 | James P. Voorhees | 1895 |
| John Tyler | Virginia | Mar. | 4, 1841–Apr. 4, 1841 | William C. McCauslen | 1898 |
| George M. Dallas | Pennsylvania | Mar. | 4, 1845–Mar. 3, 1849 | Henry J. Ellicott | 1893 |
| Millard Fillmore | New York | Mar. | 5, 1849–July 9, 1850 | Robert Cushing | 1895 |
| William R. King | Alabama | Mar. | 4, 1853–Apr. 18, 1853 | William C. McCauslen | 1896 |
| John C. Breckinridge | Kentucky | Mar. | 4, 1857–Mar. 3, 1861 | James P. Voorhees | 1896 |
| Hannibal Hamlin | Maine | Mar. | 4, 1861–Mar. 3, 1865 | Franklin Simmons | 1889 |
| Andrew Johnson | Tennessee | Mar. | 4, 1865–Apr. 15, 1865 | William C. McCauslen | 1900 |
| Schuyler Colfax | Indiana | Mar. | 4, 1869–Mar. 3, 1873 | Frances M. Goodwin | 1897 |
| Henry Wilson | Massachusetts | Mar. | 4, 1873–Nov. 22, 1875 | Daniel Chester French | 1885–86 |
| William A. Wheeler | New York | Mar. | 5, 1877–Mar. 3, 1881 | Edward C. Potter | 1892 |
| Chester A. Arthur | New York | Mar. | 4, 1881–Sept. 19, 1881 | Augustus Saint-Gaudens | 1892 |
| Thomas A. Hendricks | Indiana | Mar. | 4, 1885–Nov. 25, 1885 | U. S. J. Dunbar | 1890 |
| Levi P. Morton | New York | Mar. | 4, 1889–Mar. 3, 1893 | F. Edwin Elwell | 1891 |
| Adlai E. Stevenson | Illinois | Mar. | 4, 1893–Mar. 3, 1897 | Franklin Simmons | 1894 |
| Garret A. Hobart | New Jersey | Mar. | 4, 1897–Nov. 21, 1899 | F. Edwin Elwell | 1901 |
| Theodore Roosevelt | New York | Mar. | 4, 1901–Sept. 14, 1901 | James Earle Fraser | 1910 |
| Charles W. Fairbanks | Indiana | Mar. | 4, 1905–Mar. 3, 1909 | Franklin Simmons | 1909 |
| James S. Sherman | New York | Mar. | 4, 1909–Oct. 30, 1912 | Bessie Potter Vonnoh | 1912 |
| Thomas R. Marshall | Indiana | Mar. | 4, 1913–Mar. 3, 1921 | Moses A. Wainer Dykaar | 1920 |
| Calvin Coolidge | Massachusetts | Mar. | 4, 1921–Aug. 2, 1923 | Moses A. Wainer Dykaar | 1929 |
| Charles G. Dawes | Illinois | Mar. | 4, 1925–Mar. 3, 1929 | Jo Davidson | 1935 |
| Charles Curtis | Kansas | Mar. | 4, 1929–Mar. 3, 1933 | Moses A. Wainer Dykaar | 1935 |
| John Nance Garner | Texas | Mar. | 4, 1933–Jan. 20, 1941 | James Earle Fraser | 1943 |
| Henry A. Wallace | Iowa | Jan. | 20, 1941–Jan. 20, 1945 | Jo Davidson | 1948 |
| Harry S. Truman | Missouri | Jan. | 20, 1945–Apr. 12, 1945 | Charles Keck | 1947 |
| Alben W. Barkley | Kentucky | Jan. | 20, 1949–Jan. 20, 1953 | Kalervo Kallio | 1958 |
| Richard M. Nixon | California | Jan. | 20, 1953–Jan. 20, 1961 | Gualberto Rocchi | 1965 |
| Lyndon B. Johnson | Texas | Jan. | 20, 1961–Nov. 22, 1963 | Jimilu Mason | 1966 |
| Hubert H. Humphrey | Minnesota | Jan. | 20, 1965–Jan. 20, 1969 | | |
| Spiro T. Agnew | Maryland | Jan. | 20, 1969–Oct. 10, 1973 | | |
| Gerald R. Ford | Michigan | Dec. | 6, 1973–Aug. 9, 1974 | | |
| Nelson A. Rockefeller | New York | Dec. | 19, 1974–Jan. 20, 1977 | | |

NEG. NO. 25720

JOHN ADAMS, Vice President
Daniel Chester French, 1890, 31″
Senate Chamber gallery

NEG. NO. 25721

CHESTER A. ARTHUR, Vice President
Augustus Saint-Gaudens, 1892, 30″
Senate Chamber gallery

NEG. NO. 25741

ALBEN W. BARKLEY, Vice President
Signed r. side Kalervo Kallio; 1958, 28″
Senate wing, second floor, main corridor

NEG. NO. 36378

JOHN C. BRECKINRIDGE, Vice President
Signed l. side James Paxton Voorhees, Sc.
    A.D. 1896; 30¼″
Senate Chamber gallery

200

NEG. NO. 25723

NEG. NO. 25724

AARON BURR, Vice President
Jacques Jouvenal, 1894, 30¾"
Signed r. side Jouvenal
Senate Chamber gallery

JOHN C. CALHOUN, Vice President
Theodore A. Mills, 1896, 30"
Signed l. on back Theo. A. Mills
Senate Chamber gallery

NEG. NO. 25725

NEG. NO. 25726

GEORGE CLINTON, Vice President
Vittorio A. Ciani, 1894, 29¼"
Signed l. side Victor A. Ciani, Sculptor N.Y.
Senate Chamber gallery

SCHUYLER COLFAX, Vice President
Signed front r. side Frances M. Goodwin,
1897; 30¼"
Senate Chamber gallery

NEG. NO. 25742

CALVIN COOLIDGE, Vice President
Moses A. Wainer Dykaar, 28″
Signed r. side Moses W. Dykaar, 1927
Senate wing, second floor, east corridor

NEG. NO. 25743

CHARLES CURTIS, Vice President
Moses A. Wainer Dykaar, 24″
Signed r. side Moses Dykaar, 1929
Senate wing, second floor, east corridor

NEG. NO. 25727

GEORGE M. DALLAS, Vice President
Henry J. Ellicott, 1894, 30½″
Senate Chamber gallery

NEG. NO. 25744

CHARLES G. DAWES, Vice President
Jo Davidson, 1931, 25″
Senate wing, second floor, east corridor

NEG. NO. 25745

CHARLES W. FAIRBANKS, Vice President
Signed on back Franklin Simmons, 1905; 36″
Senate wing, second floor, main corridor

NEG. NO. 25728

MILLARD FILLMORE, Vice President
Robert Cushing, 1895, 30¼″
Senate Chamber gallery

NEG. NO. 25746

JOHN N. GARNER, Vice President
James Earle Fraser, 1943, 35″
Signed l. side J. E. Fraser
S–213, Senate Reception Room

NEG. NO. 25729

ELBRIDGE GERRY, Vice President
Signed on back Herbert Adams MDCCCXCII
    [1892]; 31¾″
Senate Chamber gallery

NEG. NO. 25730

HANNIBAL HAMLIN, Vice President
Franklin Simmons, 1890, 29½''
Senate Chamber gallery

NEG. NO. 25731

THOMAS A. HENDRICKS, Vice President
U.S.J. Dunbar, 1890, 29¼''
Senate Chamber gallery

NEG. NO. 25747

GARRET A. HOBART, Vice President
F. Edwin Elwell, 39''
Signed l. front F. E. Elwell, Sc. 1901
Senate wing, second floor, main corridor

NEG. NO. 25732

THOMAS JEFFERSON, Vice President
Sir Moses Ezekiel, 1889, 29''
Senate Chamber gallery

204

NEG. NO. 25733

ANDREW JOHNSON, Vice President
William C. McCauslen, 1900, 32″
Senate Chamber gallery

NEG. NO. 25734

RICHARD M. JOHNSON, Vice President
James P. Voorhees, 31½″
Signed r. side J. P. Voorhees '95
Senate Chamber gallery

NEG. NO. 25735

WILLIAM R. KING, Vice President
William C. McCauslen, 33″
Signed r. side W. C. M'Causlen '96
Senate Chamber gallery

NEG. NO. 25749

THOMAS R. MARSHALL, Vice President
Moses A. Wainer Dykaar, 34″
Signed r. side M. A. Dykaar, Capitol 1920
Senate wing, second floor, east corridor

NEG. NO. 25750

LEVI P. MORTON, Vice President
Signed on plinth F. Edwin Elwell, Sc.; 1891,
34″
Senate wing, second floor, main corridor

NEG. NO. 25751

THEODORE ROOSEVELT, Vice President
James Earle Fraser, 1910, 36″
Signed r. side Fraser
Senate wing, second floor, main corridor

NEG. NO. 25752

JAMES S. SHERMAN, Vice President
Bessie Potter Vonnoh, 1911, 34″
Senate wing, second floor, main corridor

NEG. NO. 25753

ADLAI E. STEVENSON, Vice President
Signed on back Franklin Simmons, 1894; 36″
Senate wing, second floor, main corridor

206

NEG. NO. 25736

NEG. NO. 25754

DANIEL TOMPKINS, Vice President
Charles H. Niehaus, 1891, 31¼″
Senate Chamber gallery

HARRY S. TRUMAN, Vice President
Signed on back Charles Keck, sculptor 19–61;
  28″
Senate wing, second floor, east corridor

NEG. NO. 25737

NEG. NO. 25738

JOHN TYLER, Vice President
William C. McCauslen, 30¼″
Signed r. side W. C. M'Causlen '98
Senate Chamber gallery

MARTIN VAN BUREN, Vice President
Signed on plinth U.S.J. Dunbar, Sc. 1894; 31″
Senate Chamber gallery

NEG. NO. 25755

NEG. NO. 25739

HENRY A. WALLACE, Vice President
Signed r. side Jo Davidson, N.Y., 1947; 23″
S–213, Senate Reception Room

WILLIAM A. WHEELER, Vice President
Edward C. Potter, 1892, 30¾″
Senate Chamber gallery

NEG. NO. 25812

HENRY WILSON, Vice President
Daniel Chester French, 1886, 32″
S–214, Vice President's formal office

208

# CHIEF JUSTICES

### TEN BUSTS

Ten marble busts of Chief Justices of the United States were acquired under appropriation and other authority. Five are located in S–141, which was the Supreme Court Chamber from 1809 to 1860. Five busts were transferred to the U.S. Supreme Court Building in 1973.

| Chief Justice | State appointed from | Service | Sculptor | Date of purchase |
|---|---|---|---|---|
| John Jay | New York | 1789–95 | John Frazee | 1831 |
| John Rutledge | South Carolina | 1795 | Alexander Galt | 1858 |
| Oliver Ellsworth | Connecticut | 1796–1800 | Hezekiah Augur | 1837 |
| John Marshall | Virginia | 1801–35 | Hiram Powers | 1836 |
| Roger B. Taney | Maryland | 1836–64 | Augustus Saint-Gaudens | 1877 |
| Salmon P. Chase [1] | Ohio | 1864–73 | Thomas D. Jones | 1875 |
| Morrison R. Waite [1] | Ohio | 1874–88 | Augustus Saint-Gaudens | 1875 |
| Melville W. Fuller [1] | Illinois | 1888–1910 | William Ordway Partridge | 1891 |
| Edward D. White [1] | Louisiana | 1910–21 | Bryant Baker | 1911 |
| William Howard Taft [1] | Connecticut | 1921–30 | Bryant Baker | 1934 |

[1] Transferred to the U.S. Supreme Court Building, 1973.

NEG. NO. 34051

SALMON P. CHASE, Chief Justice
Thomas D. Jones, 34″
U.S. Supreme Court Building

NEG. NO. 34048

OLIVER ELLSWORTH, Chief Justice
Hezekiah Augur, 33″
S–141, Old Supreme Court Chamber

NEG. NO. 34053

MELVILLE W. FULLER, Chief Justice
William Ordway Partridge, 27″
Signed r. side Ordway Partridge, 1914
U.S. Supreme Court Building

NEG. NO. 34046

JOHN JAY, Chief Justice
John Frazee, 1831, 30″
Signed front of pedestal J. Frazee, fecit
S–141, Old Supreme Court Chamber

NEG. NO. 34049

JOHN MARSHALL, Chief Justice
Hiram Powers, 33″
S–141, Old Supreme Court Chamber

NEG. NO. 34047

JOHN RUTLEDGE, Chief Justice
Alexander Galt, 38″
Signed on back A. Galt, 1858
S–141, Old Supreme Court Chamber

NEG. NO. 34055

WILLIAM HOWARD TAFT, Chief Justice
Signed r. side Bryant Baker, Sc. 1932; 29″
U.S. Supreme Court Building

NEG. NO. 34050

ROGER B. TANEY, Chief Justice
Augustus Saint-Gaudens, 29″
S–141, Old Supreme Court Chamber

NEG. NO. 34052

MORRISON R. WAITE, Chief Justice
Augustus Saint-Gaudens, 31″
U.S. Supreme Court Building

NEG. NO. 34054

EDWARD D. WHITE, Chief Justice
Bryant Baker, 28″
Signed r. side P. Bryant Baker, Sculptor, 1923
U.S. Supreme Court Building

211

NEG. NO. 34636

HENRY CLAY
Albert P. Henry, after Hart, miniature, 11″
Signed on back A. P. Henry
Purchased Joint Committee on Library 1881
HB–28

NEG. NO. 25810

LAFAYETTE S. FOSTER
Charles Calverly, marble, 22″
Gift of Mrs. Foster, 1885; accepted by S. Res.
S–214, Vice President's formal office

NEG. NO. 34637

CORDELL HULL
George Conlon, 29″. Signed r. side Conlon
Gift of the Cumberland, Maryland Evening
  and Sunday Times, 1944
Accepted by S. Con. Res. 56, 78th Congress
S–213, Senate Reception Room

NEG. NO. 34638

CHARLES SUMNER
Martin Milmore, marble, 36″
Gift of Anna Shaw Curtis, 1894
Accepted by Joint Committee on Library
Senate wing, third floor, east

# BUSTS OF MEMBERS AND SPEAKERS OF THE HOUSE OF REPRESENTATIVES

TEN BUSTS

## SPEAKERS

NEG. NO. 24683

JOSEPH G. CANNON
Signed r. side Albert Jaegers, Sc., 1913; 24″
Gift of friends, 1913
Accepted by H. Res. 873, 62nd Congress
Cannon House Office Building rotunda

NEG. NO. 24684

JAMES B. (CHAMP) CLARK
Moses A. Wainer Dykaar, marble, 26″
Signed r. side M. Dykaar, Capital, 1918
Placed 1925 by H. Res. 568, 67th Congress
Cannon House Office Building rotunda

NEG. NO. 24686

NICHOLAS LONGWORTH
Moses A. Wainer Dykaar, marble, 24″
Signed r. side Moses Dykaar, 1930
Placed 1932 by H. Res. 44, 72nd Congress
Cannon House Office Building rotunda

NEG. NO. 24689

JOSEPH W. MARTIN, JR.
Suzanne Silvercruys, marble, 23″
Signed r. side Suzanne Silver, 1962
Gift of Nat'l. Federation of GOP Women, 1962
Accepted by H. Res. 393, 87th Congress
Cannon House Office Building rotunda

SAM RAYBURN
Signed l.r. Paul Manship, sculp 1964; marble,
  5′9¾′′ x 2′9′′
Purchased 1964
Rayburn House Office Building, first floor

THOMAS BRACKETT REED
Gutzon and Lincoln Borglum, marble, 26′′
Signed r. side Gutzon Borglum, Sc.
Placed 1943 by H. Res. 315, 76th Congress
Cannon House Office Building rotunda

NEG. NO. 24685

CLAUDE KITCHIN
Signed l. side Edgardo Simone; marble, 23″
Placed 1931 by H. Res. 95, 71st Congress
Cannon House Office Building rotunda

NEG. NO. 24687

MARTIN B. MADDEN
Signed l. side Albin Polasek, 1929; 21″
Placed 1929 by H. Res. 226, 70th Congress
Cannon House Office Building rotunda

NEG. NO. 24688

JAMES R. MANN
Signed r. side Herbert Adams, Sc. MCMXXV
[1925]; marble, 26″
Placed 1925 by H. Res. 568, 67th Congress
Cannon House Office Building rotunda

NEG. NO. 34639

OSCAR W. UNDERWOOD
Chester Beach, 34″. Signed l. side Beach, 1933
Placed 1933 by H. Res. 55, 72nd Congress
Cannon House Office Building rotunda

# PROMINENT INDIVIDUALS

### ELEVEN BUSTS

NEG. NO. 24553

AYSH-KE-BAH-KE-KO-ZHAY, Chippewa Chief
Signed front By Francis Vincenti; marble, 24″
By employment of artist at the Capitol, 1858
Senate wing, third floor, east corridor

NEG. NO. 181-B

NEG. NO. 25071

BEESHEKEE (Buffalo), Chippewa warrior
Joseph Lassalle after Vincenti, bronze, 25″
By employment of artist at Capitol, 1858
House wing, west stairway, first floor

BEESHEKEE (Buffalo)
Francis Vincenti, marble, 33″
By employment of artist at Capitol, 1854
Senate wing, third floor, east corridor

NEG. NO. 32125

CONSTANTINO BRUMIDI
Signed l. side Jimilu Mason © 1967; marble, 28''
Purchased 1966 by the Joint Committee on the
Library by S. Con. Res. 70, 89th Congress
Brumidi corridor, Senate wing, first floor

Brumidi spent 25 years decorating the capitol.

NEG. NO. 24555

VISCOUNT JAMES BRYCE
Sir William Reid Dick, bronze, 31''
Gift of Sir Charles Cheers Wakefield for the
Sulgrave Institution of Great Britain, 1922
Accepted by Joint Committee on Library
Senate wing, third floor, east

Ambassador from Great Britain to the U.S. 1907–13.

NEG. NO. 34642

THOMAS CRAWFORD
Tommaso Gagliardi, marble, 34''
Signed on back T. Gagliardi, fecit
Purchased 1871
Senate wing, third floor, east

Crawford, an American sculptor, is represented in
the Capitol by many works of art.

NEG. NO. 23305

GIUSEPPE GARIBALDI
Giuseppe Martegana, marble, 32''
Signed back of bust Martegana
Gift of members of the Italian Society of
Washington, Citizens of Italian descent, 1888
Accepted by Joint Committee on Library
Lobby opposite entrance to S–141

Italian patriot and soldier, who unified Italy.

NEG. NO. 24557

JOHN PAUL JONES
Antoine Houdon, bronze, 28"
Gift of the Secretary of the Navy, 1948
Accepted by the Joint Committee on the Library
Senate wing, third floor, east

American Naval Officer in Revolutionary War. Bust
was cast in 1904 from original 1780 plaster model.

NEG. NO. 23302

THADDEUS KOSCIUSZKO
H. Dmochowski-Saunders, marble, 35"
Signed r. base H. D. Saunders, 1857
Purchased 1857
Lobby opposite entrance to S–141

Polish-American patriot and statesman, who served
in the Revolutionary War.

NEG. NO. 34640

GENERAL LAFAYETTE
Signed r. side P. J. David d'Angers, 1830;
    marble, 33". Purchased 1904
Rotunda

French patriot who assisted George Washington during American Revolution. This marble bust replaced the
original one destroyed in the Library fire of 1851.

NEG. NO. 23304

K. K. (CASIMIR) PULASKI
H. Dmochowski-Saunders, marble, 39"
Signed l. base H. Dmochowski, 1857, PHI
Purchased 1882
Lobby opposite entrance to S–141

Polish-American Revolutionary War patriot. Earned
the right of American citizenship by giving his life at the
siege of Savannah in 1779.

218

# NATIONAL STATUARY HALL

The concept of a National Statuary Hall began in the middle of the nineteenth century. The completion of the present House wing in 1857 allowed the House of Representatives to move into its new and larger chamber. The old, vacant, semicircular, marble columned chamber became a cluttered thorough fare between the Rotunda and the House wing.

Suggestions for the use of the old chamber were made as early as 1853 by Gouverneur Kemble, a former member of the House, who pressed for its use as a gallery for historical paintings. The space between the columns seemed too limited for such a purpose, but was considered more suited for the display of busts and statuary.

On April 19, 1864, the Honorable Justin S. Morrill in the House of Representatives proposed: "To what end more useful or grand, and at the same time simple and inexpensive, can we devote it [the Chamber] than to ordain that it shall be set apart for the reception of such statuary as each State shall elect to be deserving of in this lasting commemoration?"

This proposal was enacted into the law creating the National Statuary Hall, July 2, 1864 (sec. 1814 of the Revised Statutes), the essential part of which provides:

And the President is hereby authorized to invite each and all the States to provide and furnish statues, in marble or bronze, not exceeding two in number for each State, of deceased persons who have been citizens thereof, and illustrious for their historic renown or for distinguished civic or military services such as each State may deem to be worthy of this national commemoration; and when so furnished the same shall be placed in the Old Hall of the House of Representatives, in the Capitol of the United States, which is set apart, or so much thereof as may be necessary, as a national statuary hall for the purpose herein indicated.

By 1933, 65 statues were crowded into Statuary Hall. In some places they were lined three deep which was esthetically displeasing. More important, however, the structure of the chamber would not accommodate the excessive weight and there were statues yet to come.

On February 24, 1933, Congress passed House Concurrent Resolution No. 47 to provide for the relocation of statues and to govern the future reception and location of statues.

Resolved by the House of Representatives (the Senate concurring), That the Architect of the Capitol, upon the approval of the Joint Committee on the Library, with the advice of the Commission of Fine Arts, is hereby authorized and directed to relocate within the Capitol any of the statues already received and placed in Statuary Hall, and to provide for the reception and location of the statues received hereafter from the States.

Under authority of this resolution, it was decided that only one statue from each State should be placed in Statuary Hall. The other statues were located prominently in designated areas and corridors of the Capitol.

A second rearrangement of the statues was made in 1976 by authorization of the Joint Committee on the Library to reduce overcrowding and to improve the aesthetic quality and orderliness of the physical arrangement of the National Statuary Hall Collection. Statues were placed in the East Central Hall of the east front extension on the first floor of the Capitol. Other statues were relocated within the corridors, Hall of Columns and Statuary Hall.

Ninety-two statues, 45 marble and 47 bronze, have been contributed by 50 States. Two statues have been contributed by 41 States. One statue has been received from each of the following 8 States: Colorado, Montana, Nevada, New Mexico, North Dakota, Utah, Washington and Wyoming.

# ALPHABETICAL LIST OF THE 92 STATUES IN THE NATIONAL STATUARY HALL COLLECTION

| Statue | State | Sculptor | Medium | Unveiling or congressional proceedings | Location |
|--------|-------|----------|--------|----------------------------------------|----------|
| Adams, Samuel | Massachusetts | Anne Whitney | Marble | Congressional Proceedings 1876 | E. Central Hall |
| Allen, Ethan | Vermont | Larkin G. Mead | Marble | Congressional Proceedings 1876 | Statuary Hall |
| Allen, William | Ohio | Charles H. Niehaus | Marble | Placed 1887 | Statuary Hall |
| Austin, Stephen F. | Texas | Elisabet Ney | Marble | Congressional Proceedings 1905 | Small House rotunda |
| Aycock, Charles Brantley | North Carolina | Charles Keck | Bronze | Unveiled 1932 | E. Central Hall |
| Bartlett, E. L. "Bob" | Alaska | Felix W. de Weldon | Bronze | Unveiled 1971 | House connecting corridor |
| Beadle, William H. H. | South Dakota | H. Daniel Webster | Bronze | Unveiled 1938 | Statuary Hall |
| Benton, Thomas H. | Missouri | Alexander Doyle | Marble | Congressional Proceedings 1899 | Statuary Hall |
| Blair, Francis P., Jr. | Missouri | Alexander Doyle | Marble | Congressional Proceedings 1899 | Hall of Columns |
| Borah, William E. | Idaho | Bryant Baker | Bronze | Unveiled 1947 | Senate connecting corridor |
| Bryan, William Jennings | Nebraska | Rudulph Evans | Bronze | Unveiled 1937 | Statuary Hall |
| Burke, John | North Dakota | Avard Fairbanks | Bronze | Unveiled 1963 | Statuary Hall |
| Calhoun, John C. | South Carolina | Frederic W. Ruckstull | Marble | Unveiled 1910 | E. Central Hall |
| Carroll, Charles, of Carrollton | Maryland | Richard E. Brooks | Bronze | Congressional Proceedings 1903 | E. Central Hall |
| Cass, Lewis | Michigan | Daniel Chester French | Marble | Congressional Proceedings 1889 | Statuary Hall |
| Chandler, Zachariah | Michigan | Charles H. Niehaus | Marble | Unveiled 1913 | Hall of Columns |
| Chavez, Dennis | New Mexico | Felix W. de Weldon | Bronze | Unveiled 1966 | Vestibule north of Rotunda |
| Clarke, James P. | Arkansas | Pompeo Coppini | Marble | Placed 1921 | Hall of Columns |
| Clay, Henry | Kentucky | Charles H. Niehaus | Bronze | Unveiled 1929 | Statuary Hall |
| Clayton, John M. | Delaware | Bryant Baker | Marble | Unveiled 1934 | Senate connecting corridor |
| Clinton, George | New York | Henry Kirke Brown | Bronze | Placed 1873 | Small House rotunda |
| Collamer, Jacob | Vermont | Preston Powers | Marble | Congressional Proceedings 1881 | Hall of Columns |
| Curry, Jabez Lamar Monroe | Alabama | Dante Sodini | Marble | Congressional Proceedings 1908 | Hall of Columns |
| Damien, Father | Hawaii | Marisol Escobar | Bronze | Unveiled 1969 | Hall of Columns |
| Davis, Jefferson | Mississippi | Augustus Lukeman | Bronze | Unveiled 1931 | Statuary Hall |
| Fulton, Robert | Pennsylvania | Howard Roberts | Marble | Congressional Proceedings 1889 | Statuary Hall |
| Garfield, James A. | Ohio | Charles H. Niehaus | Marble | Congressional Proceedings 1886 | Rotunda |
| George, James Z. | Mississippi | Augustus Lukeman | Bronze | Unveiled 1931 | Hall of Columns |
| Glick, George W. | Kansas | Charles H. Niehaus | Marble | Congressional Proceedings 1914 | Hall of Columns |
| Gorrie, John | Florida | C. A. Pillars | Marble | Unveiled 1914 | Statuary Hall |
| Greene, Nathanael | Rhode Island | Henry Kirke Brown | Marble | Congressional Proceedings 1870 | E. Central Hall |
| Greenway, John C. | Arizona | Gutzon Borglum | Bronze | Unveiled 1930 | Statuary Hall |
| Gruening, Ernest | Alaska | George Anthonisen | Bronze | Unveiled 1977 | Hall of Columns |
| Hamlin, Hannibal | Maine | Charles E. Tefft | Bronze | Unveiled 1935 | Statuary Hall |

| Statue | State | Sculptor | Medium | Unveiling or congressional proceedings | Location |
| --- | --- | --- | --- | --- | --- |
| Hampton, Wade | South Carolina | Frederic W. Ruckstull | Marble | Unveiled 1929 | House connecting corridor |
| Hanson, John | Maryland | Richard E. Brooks | Bronze | Congressional Proceedings (1903) | Senate connecting corridor |
| Harlan, James | Iowa | Nellie V. Walker | Bronze | Installed 1910 | Hall of Columns |
| Houston, Samuel | Texas | Elisabet Ney | Marble | Congressional Proceedings 1905 | Statuary Hall |
| Ingalls, John J. | Kansas | Charles H. Niehaus | Marble | Congressional Proceedings 1905 | Statuary Hall |
| Jackson, Andrew | Tennessee | Belle Kinney Scholz and Leopold F. Scholz | Bronze | Unveiled 1928 | Rotunda |
| Kamehameha I | Hawaii | Thomas R. Gould | Bronze | Unveiled 1969 | Statuary Hall |
| Kearny, Philip | New Jersey | Henry Kirke Brown | Bronze | Congressional Proceedings 1888 | Hall of Columns |
| Kenna, John E. | West Virginia | Alexander Doyle | Marble | Placed 1901 | Hall of Columns |
| King, Thomas Starr | California | Haig Patigian | Bronze | Unveiled 1931 | Hall of Columns |
| King, William | Maine | Franklin Simmons | Marble | Congressional Proceedings 1878 | House connecting corridor |
| Kino, Eusebio F. | Arizona | Suzanne Silvercruys | Bronze | Unveiled 1965 | Hall of Columns |
| Kirkwood, Samuel J. | Iowa | Vinnie Ream | Bronze | Placed 1913 | Statuary Hall |
| La Follette, Robert M., | Wisconsin | Jo Davidson | Marble | Unveiled 1929 | Statuary Hall |
| Lee, Rev. Jason | Oregon | Gifford Proctor [1] | Bronze | Unveiled 1953 | Statuary Hall |
| Lee, Robert E. | Virginia | Edward V. Valentine | Bronze | Unveiled 1934 | Statuary Hall |
| Livingston, Robert R. | New York | Erastus Dow Palmer | Bronze | Placed 1875 | E. Central Hall |
| Long, Dr. Crawford W. | Georgia | J. Massey Rhind | Marble | Unveiled 1926 | E. Central Hall |
| Long, Huey P. | Louisiana | Charles Keck | Bronze | Unveiled 1941 | Statuary Hall |
| Marquette, Pere Jacques | Wisconsin | Gaetano Trentanove | Marble | Congressional Proceedings 1896 | House connecting corridor |
| McCarran, Patrick A. | Nevada | Yolande Jacobson | Bronze | Unveiled 1960 | Statuary Hall vestibule north |
| McDowell, Dr. Ephraim | Kentucky | Charles H. Niehaus | Bronze | Unveiled 1929 | Senate connecting corridor |
| McLoughlin, Dr. John | Oregon | Gifford Proctor [1] | Bronze | Unveiled 1953 | House connecting corridor |
| Morris, Esther H. | Wyoming | Avard Fairbanks | Bronze | Unveiled 1960 | Statuary Hall vestibule north |
| Morton J. Sterling | Nebraska | Rudulph Evans | Bronze | Unveiled 1937 | Hall of Columns |
| Morton, Oliver P. | Indiana | Charles H. Niehaus | Marble | Congressional Proceedings 1900 | Hall of Columns |
| Muhlenberg, John P. G. | Pennsylvania | Blanche Nevin | Marble | Congressional Proceedings 1889 | Small House rotunda |
| Pierpont, Francis H. | West Virginia | Franklin Simmons | Marble | Unveiled 1910 | Statuary Hall |
| Rice, Henry Mower | Minnesota | Frederick E. Triebel | Marble | Unveiled 1916 | Statuary Hall |
| Rodney, Caesar | Delaware | Bryant Baker | Marble | Unveiled 1934 | E. Central Hall |
| Rogers, Will | Oklahoma | Jo Davidson | Bronze | Unveiled 1939 | House connecting corridor |

[1] Joint commission for the Oregon statues was given to A. Phimister Proctor and his son, Gifford. Phimister died before the models were completed and the statues were executed by Gifford (G. MacG.).

| Statue | State | Sculptor | Medium | Unveiling or congressional proceedings | Location |
|---|---|---|---|---|---|
| Rose, Uriah M. | Arkansas | Frederic W. Ruckstuhl | Marble | Placed 1917 | Statuary Hall |
| Russell, Charles M. | Montana | John B. Weaver | Bronze | Unveiled 1959 | Statuary Hall |
| Sabin, Dr. Florence R. | Colorado | Joy Buba | Bronze | Unveiled 1959 | Statuary Hall |
| Sanford, Maria L. | Minnesota | Evelyn Raymond | Bronze | Unveiled 1958 | Senate connecting corridor |
| Sequoyah (Sequoya) | Oklahoma | Vinnie Ream (completed by G. Julian Zolnay) | Bronze | Unveiled 1917 | Statuary Hall |
| Serra, Junipero | California | Ettore Cadorin | Bronze | Unveiled 1931 | Statuary Hall |
| Sevier, John | Tennessee | Belle Kinney Scholz and Leopold F. Scholz | Bronze | Unveiled 1931 | Statuary Hall |
| Sherman, Roger | Connecticut | Chauncey B. Ives | Marble | Congressional Proceedings 1872 | E. Central Hall |
| Shields, Gen. James | Illinois | Leonard W. Volk | Bronze | Unveiled 1893 | Hall of Columns |
| Shoup, George L. | Idaho | Frederick E. Triebel | Marble | Congressional Proceedings 1910 | Statuary Hall |
| Smith, Gen. E. Kirby | Florida | C. Adrian Pillars | Bronze | Congressional Proceedings 1922 | Hall of Columns |
| Stark, John | New Hampshire | Carl Conrads | Marble | Congressional Proceedings 1894 | Vestibule north of Rotunda |
| Stephens, Alexander H. | Georgia | Gutzon Borglum | Marble | Unveiled 1927 | Statuary Hall |
| Stockton, Richard | New Jersey | Henry Kirke Brown (completed by H. K. Bush-Brown) | Marble | Congressional Proceedings 1888 | E. Central Hall |
| Trumbull, Jonathan | Connecticut | Chauncey B. Ives | Marble | Congressional Proceedings 1872 | House connecting corridor |
| Vance, Zebulon Baird | North Carolina | Gutzon Borglum | Bronze | Unveiled 1916 | Statuary Hall |
| Wallace, General Lew | Indiana | Andrew O'Connor | Marble | Unveiled 1910 | Statuary Hall |
| Ward, Joseph | South Dakota | Bruno Beghé | Marble | Unveiled 1963 | Hall of Columns |
| Washington, George | Virginia | Antoine Houdon | Bronze | Unveiled 1934 | Rotunda |
| Webster, Daniel | New Hampshire | Carl Conrads (after Thomas Ball) | Marble | Congressional Proceedings 1894 | Statuary Hall |
| Wheeler, General Joseph | Alabama | Berthold Nebel | Bronze | Unveiled 1925 | Statuary Hall |
| White, Edward Douglass | Louisiana | Arthur C. Morgan | Bronze | Unveiled 1955 | Senate connecting corridor |
| Whitman, Marcus | Washington | Avard Fairbanks | Bronze | Unveiled 1953 | Statuary Hall |
| Willard, Frances E. | Illinois | Helen Farnsworth Mears | Marble | Congressional Proceedings 1905 | Statuary Hall |
| Williams, Roger | Rhode Island | Franklin Simmons | Marble | Congressional Proceedings 1872 | E. Central Hall |
| Winthrop, John | Massachusetts | Richard S. Greenough | Marble | Congressional Proceedings 1876 | Hall of Columns |
| Young, Brigham | Utah | Mahonri Young | Marble | Unveiled 1950 | Statuary Hall |

# LOCATIONS OF STATUES

## 40 STATUES IN STATUARY HALL

| State | Statue | Sculptor |
|-------|--------|----------|
| Alabama | General Joseph Wheeler | Berthold Nebel |
| Arizona | John Campbell Greenway | Gutzon Borglum |
| Arkansas | Uriah M. Rose | Frederic W. Ruckstuhl |
| California | Junipero Serra | Ettore Cadorin |
| Colorado | Dr. Florence Rena Sabin | Joy Buba |
| Florida | John Gorrie | Charles Adrian Pillars |
| Georgia | Alexander H. Stephens | Gutzon Borglum |
| Hawaii | King Kamehameha I | Thomas R. Gould |
| Idaho | George L. Shoup | Frederick Ernst Triebel |
| Illinois | Frances E. Willard | Helen Farnsworth Mears |
| Indiana | General Lew Wallace | Andrew O'Connor |
| Iowa | Samuel J. Kirkwood | Vinnie Ream |
| Kansas | John J. Ingalls | Charles H. Niehaus |
| Kentucky | Henry Clay | Charles H. Niehaus |
| Louisiana | Huey P. Long | Charles Keck |
| Maine | Hannibal Hamlin | Charles E. Tefft |
| Michigan | Lewis Cass | Daniel Chester French |
| Minnesota | Henry M. Rice | Frederick Ernst Triebel |
| Mississippi | Jefferson Davis | Augustus Lukeman |
| Missouri | Thomas H. Benton | Alexander Doyle |
| Montana | Charles Marion Russell | John B. Weaver |
| Nebraska | William Jennings Bryan | Rudulph Evans |
| Nevada | Patrick A. McCarran | Yolande Jacobson |
| New Hampshire | Daniel Webster | Carl Conrads |
| North Carolina | Zebulon B. Vance | Gutzon Borglum |
| North Dakota | John Burke | Avard Fairbanks |
| Ohio | William Allen | Charles H. Niehaus |
| Oklahoma | Sequoyah (Sequoya) | Vinnie Ream |
| Oregon | Rev. Jason Lee | Gifford MacG. Proctor |
| Pennsylvania | Robert Fulton | Howard Roberts |
| South Dakota | Gen. William Henry H. Beadle | H. Daniel Webster |
| Tennessee | John Sevier | Belle K. and L. F. Scholz |
| Texas | Samuel Houston | Elisabet Ney |
| Utah | Brigham Young | Mahronri Young |
| Vermont | Ethan Allen | Larkin G. Mead |
| Virginia | Robert E. Lee | Edward V. Valentine |
| Washington | Marcus Whitman | Avard Fairbanks |
| West Virginia | Francis H. Pierpont | Franklin Simmons |
| Wisconsin | Robert M. La Follette, Sr. | Jo Davidson |
| Wyoming | Esther H. Morris | Avard Fairbanks |

| State | Statue | Sculptor |
| --- | --- | --- |

## 3 STATUES IN THE ROTUNDA

| | | |
| --- | --- | --- |
| Ohio | James A. Garfield | Charles H. Niehaus |
| Tennessee | Andrew Jackson | Belle K. Scholz and L. F. Scholz |
| Virginia | George Washington | Antoine Houdon |

## 3 STATUES IN THE SMALL HOUSE ROTUNDA

| | | |
| --- | --- | --- |
| New York | George Clinton | Henry Kirke Brown |
| Pennsylvania | J. P. G. Muhlenberg | Blanche Nevin |
| Texas | Stephen F. Austin | Elisabet Ney |

## 2 STATUES IN THE VESTIBULE NORTH OF THE ROTUNDA

| | | |
| --- | --- | --- |
| New Hampshire | John Stark | Carl Conrads |
| New Mexico | Dennis Chavez | Felix W. de Weldon |

## 6 STATUES IN THE SENATE CONNECTING CORRIDOR

| | | |
| --- | --- | --- |
| Delaware | John M. Clayton | Bryant Baker |
| Idaho | William E. Borah | Bryant Baker |
| Kentucky | Dr. Ephraim McDowell | Charles H. Niehaus |
| Louisiana | Edward D. White | Arthur C. Morgan |
| Maryland | John Hanson | Richard E. Brooks |
| Minnesota | Maria L. Sanford | Evelyn Raymond |

## 7 STATUES IN THE HOUSE CONNECTING CORRIDOR

| | | |
| --- | --- | --- |
| Alaska | E. L. "Bob" Bartlett | Felix W. de Weldon |
| Connecticut | Jonathan Trumbull | Chauncey B. Ives |
| Maine | William King | Franklin Simmons |
| Oklahoma | Will Rogers | Jo Davidson |
| Oregon | Dr. John McLoughlin | Gifford MacG. Proctor |
| South Carolina | Wade Hampton | Frederic W. Ruckstull |
| Wisconsin | Pere Jacques Marquette | Gaetano Trentanove |

## 10 STATUES IN THE EAST CENTRAL HALL

| | | |
| --- | --- | --- |
| Connecticut | Roger Sherman | Chauncey B. Ives |
| Delaware | Caesar Rodney | Bryant Baker |
| Georgia | Dr. Crawford W. Long | J. Massey Rhind |
| Massachusetts | Samuel Adams | Anne Whitney |
| Maryland | Charles Carroll of Carrollton | Richard E. Brooks |
| New Jersey | Richard Stockton | Henry K. Brown |
| New York | Robert R. Livingston | Erastus D. Palmer |
| North Carolina | Charles B. Aycock | Charles Keck |
| Rhode Island | Nathanael Greene | Henry K. Brown |
| South Carolina | John C. Calhoun | Frederic W. Ruckstuhl |

| State | Statue | Sculptor |
|---|---|---|

## 20 STATUES IN THE HALL OF COLUMNS

| State | Statue | Sculptor |
|---|---|---|
| Alabama | J. L. M. Curry | Dante Sodini |
| Alaska | Ernest Greuning | George Anthonisen |
| Arizona | Eusebio F. Kino | Suzanne Silvercruys |
| Arkansas | James P. Clarke | Pompeo Coppini |
| California | Thomas Starr King | Haig Patigian |
| Florida | General Edmund Kirby Smith | Charles Adrian Pillars |
| Hawaii | Father Damien | Marisol Escobar |
| Illinois | General James Shields | Leonard W. Volk |
| Indiana | Oliver P. Morton | Charles H. Niehaus |
| Iowa | James Harlan | Nellie V. Walker |
| Kansas | George W. Glick | Charles H. Niehaus |
| Massachusetts | John Winthrop | Richard S. Greenough |
| Michigan | Zachariah Chandler | Charles H. Niehaus |
| Mississippi | James Z. George | Augustus Lukeman |
| Missouri | Francis P. Blair, Jr. | Alexander Doyle |
| Nebraska | J. Sterling Morton | Rudulph Evans |
| New Jersey | General Philip Kearny | Henry Kirke Brown |
| Rhode Island | Roger Williams | Franklin Simmons |
| South Dakota | Joseph Ward | Bruno Beghé |
| Vermont | Jacob Collamer | Preston Powers |
| West Virginia | John E. Kenna | Alexander Doyle |

NEG. NO. 27437

NEG. NO. 35019

SAMUEL ADAMS, 1722–1803, Massachusetts
Signed back of base Anne Whitney; back of
    tree stump A. W. Boston, 1876; marble, 7′8″
East Central Hall

Patriot and called "Father of the American Revolution" and signer of the Declaration of Independence. Member of General Court of Mass. 1765–74; Continental Congress 1774–82; Mass. Constitutional Convention 1779; president of Mass. State senate 1781; member of state convention which ratified U.S. Constitution 1788; Lieutenant-Governor of Mass. 1789–94; Governor 1794–97.

ETHAN ALLEN, 1737–1789, Vermont
Larkin G. Mead, executed about 1874–75,
    marble, 8′8″
Signed back of base L. G. Mead
Statuary Hall

Revolutionary soldier and author. Served in the French and Indian War; Colonel of the Green Mountain Boys 1770; caused Fort Ticonderoga to surrender 1775; rose to rank of Brigadier General in the Vermont Militia; prepared Vermont for admission into the Federal Union.

228

NEG. NO. 27433

NEG. NO. 35020

STEPHEN F. AUSTIN, 1793–1836, Texas
Signed r. base Elisabet Ney, fec., Austin, Texas,
  1904; marble, 6′2″
Small House rotunda

WILLIAM ALLEN, 1803–1879, Ohio
Charles H. Niehaus, 1885–87, marble, 7′5″
Signed l. base Niehaus
Statuary Hall

  Lawyer, statesman, Governor. Member of the U.S.
House of Representatives 1833–35; member of the U.S.
Senate 1837–49; Governor 1874–76.

  Colonizer and patriot. Under a contract with Mexico,
was given judicial and military control of the local
Mexican State of Texas. He assisted in bringing about the
recognition of Texas independence 1836. As Secretary
of the Lone Star Republic of Texas he paved the way for
annexation to the United States, but did not live to see it
accomplished.

229

NEG. NO. 35021

CHARLES BRANTLEY AYCOCK, 1859–1912, North Carolina

Signed l. base Charles Keck, Sc.; executed 1929–32, bronze, 7′3″

East Central Hall

Lawyer, educator and Governor. Superintendent of Public Instruction, Wayne County 1881; U.S. district attorney 1893–97; Governor of North Carolina 1901–05.

NEG. NO. 35022

EDWARD LEWIS "BOB" BARTLETT, 1904–1968, Alaska

Signed r. base Felix De Weldon, S.C., 1971; bronze, 8′6″

House connecting corridor

Reporter, gold miner, Secretary of Alaska, Delegate to Congress 1945–59; U.S. Senator 1959–68. His instrumentality in gaining Statehood for Alaska has given him the title "Architect of Alaska Statehood."

NEG. NO. 35023

WILLIAM HENRY HARRISON BEADLE, 1838–1915,
South Dakota

Signed front base of column Copyright by the
Sculptor H. Daniel Webster 1911; bronze,
6′4″

Statuary Hall

Educator, conservationist, statesman, soldier, lawyer,
engineer. Instrumental in saving 20 million acres of
school lands in S. Dak., N. Dak., Mont., Wash., Idaho
and Wyoming from speculators. Territorial superintendent of Public Instruction, 1879, and president of
Madison Normal School. Rose from enlisted man to
Brigadier General in the Civil War.

NEG. NO. 35024

THOMAS HART BENTON, 1782–1858, Missouri
Alexander Doyle, executed 1895–97, marble,
7′7″

Statuary Hall

Author, lawyer, statesman. Member of tne Tenn.
legislature 1809–11; Aide-de-camp to General Jackson
in the War of 1812; editor of the "Missouri Inquirer";
U.S. Senator 1821–51; member of the U.S. House of
Representatives 1853–55, and author of *The Thirty
Years View*, and *Abridgment of the Debates of Congress
from 1789–1850*.

231

NEG. NO. 28000

NEG. NO. 35025

FRANCIS P. BLAIR, JR., 1821–1875, Missouri
Alexander Doyle, executed 1895–97, marble,
    7′6″
Hall of Columns

Soldier, lawyer and statesman; served in War with
Mexico. Member of the Missouri general assembly;
served in the U.S. House of Representatives intermittently from 1852 to 1864, and the U.S. Senate 1871–73.

WILLIAM EDGAR BORAH, 1865–1940, Idaho
Signed top r. base Bryant Baker, Sculptor, 1946;
    bronze, 7′2″
Senate connecting corridor

Lawyer, legislator, statesman and orator. Renown for
his distinguished service in foreign affairs; U.S. Senator
1907–40. Known as the Lone Lion of Idaho.

NEG. NO. 35026

NEG. NO. 35027

WILLIAM JENNINGS BRYAN, 1860–1925, Nebraska
Rudulph Evans, executed 1936–37, bronze,
6'7''
Signed r. base R. Evans
Statuary Hall

Soldier, lawyer, orator and statesman. Member of the
U.S. House of Representatives 1891–95; 3 times an
unsuccessful candidate for President of the United States;
Colonel in the Spanish-American War 1898; founder of
The Commoner newspaper 1901; a zealous worker in
religious and civic interests; Secretary of State under
President Wilson 1913–15.

JOHN BURKE, 1859–1937, North Dakota
Signed r. base Avard Fairbanks, 1962; bronze,
8'6''
Statuary Hall

"North Dakota's Lincoln"; jurist, statesman; State
representative 1890; State senator 1892; Governor 1906;
Treasurer of the U.S. 1913–21 under Woodrow Wilson;
chief justice of the State supreme court.

233

NEG. NO. 35028

JOHN C. CALHOUN, 1782–1850, South Carolina
Frederic W. Ruckstuhl, marble, 7′7″
Signed r. base F. W. RUCKSTUHL, S.C./1909
East Central Hall

Lawyer, statesman, orator and Vice President of the United States; leader of a school of earnest men who believed secession was warranted or at least permissible under the Constitution of the United States because not expressly forbidden. State house of representatives 1808–09; U.S. House of Representatives 1811–17; Secretary of War 1817–25; Vice President 1825–32; U.S. Senator 1832–43, 1845–50; Secretary of State 1844–45.

CHARLES CARROLL OF CARROLLTON, 1737–1832, Maryland
Signed l. base Richard E. Brooks, Sc., Paris MCMII [1902]; bronze, 7′6″
East Central Hall

Lawyer, patriot, statesman and signer of the Declaration of Independence. Commissioner to Canada 1776; delegate to the Continental Congress 1776–78; Member of Maryland state senate 1777–1800. U.S. Senator 1789–92; and was the last surviving signer of the Declaration of Independence.

NEG. NO. 27492

NEG. NO. 27521

LEWIS CASS, 1782–1866, Michigan
Daniel Chester French, marble, 7′8″
Signed l. base D. C. French, 1888, Sculptor
Statuary Hall

Soldier, diplomat and statesman. Member of the Ohio house of representatives; Brigadier General during the War of 1812; Governor of Territory of Michigan 1813–1831. Secretary of War under Jackson 1831–36; U.S. Minister to France 1836–42; U.S. Senator 1845–48, 1849–57; and Secretary of State under Buchanan 1857–60; an unsuccessful candidate for President. He left the Cabinet of Buchanan when secession was imminent.

ZACHARIAH CHANDLER, 1813–1879, Michigan
Charles H. Niehaus, executed 1912, marble, 7′7″
Hall of Columns

Opposed secession and slavery above all else; aided in organizing the Republican Party; U.S. Senator 1857–75; became the confidant of Lincoln and steadfastly advocated the principles of his party. Secretary of Interior 1875–77 under President Grant.

NEG. NO. 35029

NEG. NO. 28001

DENNIS CHAVEZ, 1888–1962, New Mexico
Signed top l. base Felix de Weldon, Sc.; exe-
cuted 1966, bronze, 7′5″
Vestibule north of Rotunda

Lawyer, U.S. Representative 1931–35; U.S. Senator
1935–62. Served in New Mexico legislature and introduced the first bill to provide free textbooks in the public
schools. Proud of his Spanish ancestry, received the
Order of Aztec Eagle from the Mexican Government;
influenced legislation establishing the Pan-American
highway.

JAMES P. CLARKE, 1854–1916, Arkansas
Signed r. base Pompeo Coppini, Sculptor,
Chicago; executed 1917–21, marble, 6′10″
Hall of Columns

Lawyer, State attorney general, Governor of Arkansas,
and U.S. Senator from March 4, 1903 until the time of
his death, October 1, 1916; served as President pro
tempore of the Senate 1913–16.

236

NEG. NO. 35030

NEG. NO. 27493

HENRY CLAY, 1777–1852, Kentucky
Charles H. Niehaus, bronze, 7′2″
Signed r. base C. H. Niehaus, Sculptor, 1928
Statuary Hall

Lawyer, statesman, parliamentarian, orator. U.S. Senator 1806–07 (in contravention of the 30-year age requirement of the Constitution) and also served intermittently from 1810 until his death in 1852. Member of the Kentucky legislature 1808–09; U.S. House of Representatives intermittently 1811 to 1825. Chosen to the Speakership the day he became a Member, an unprecedented distinction. Peace Commissioner to Great Britain 1814; Secretary of State under John Quincy Adams 1825–29.

JOHN M. CLAYTON, 1796–1856, Delaware
Signed l. base Bryant Baker, Sc. 1932; marble, 7′6″
Senate connecting corridor

Noted as a jurist, a statesman and a diplomat. State house of representatives, secretary of state and chief justice; Member of the U.S. Senate 1829–36 and 1845–49, when he resigned to accept position of Secretary of State under President Taylor; negotiated the Clayton-Bulwer Treaty; again elected to the U.S. Senate 1853 until his death.

NEG. NO. 35031

NEG. NO. 28002

GEORGE CLINTON, 1739–1812, New York
Henry Kirke Brown, bronze, 6′8′′
Signed front base H. K. Brown, Sculpt. 1873
Small House rotunda

Lawyer, soldier, Governor and Vice President. Fought in the French and Indian War and as a Brigadier General in the Revolutionary War; delegate to the Continental Congress, 1775; first Governor of N.Y. 1777–95, 1801–1804; President of the N.Y. convention ratifying the U.S. Constitution; and Vice President of the U.S. under both Jefferson and Madison.

JACOB COLLAMER, 1792–1865, Vermont
Preston Powers, marble, 6′8′′
Signed r. base P. Powers, Sculp. 1879
Hall of Columns

Soldier, orator, jurist, statesman. Served in the War of 1812; Member of the State house of representatives, 1821–22, 1827–28; State's attorney 1822–24; Judge of the Superior Court, 1833–42; 1850–54; elected to U.S. House of Representatives 1843–49; Postmaster General under Taylor 1849–50; U.S. Senator 1855–65.

NEG. NO. 35032

NEG. NO. 35034

JABEZ, LAMAR MONROE CURRY, 1825–1903, Alabama

Signed r. base Dante Sodini, Florence, Italy; 1904–06, marble, 7'4''

Hall of Columns

Soldier, statesman, educator and orator; served in the War with Mexico and the Civil War; Member of the U.S. House of Representatives 1857–61; resigned to become a member of the Confederate Congress 1861–64; professor and college president; Minister to Spain.

FATHER DAMIEN SS.CC., 1840–1889, Hawaii

Marisol Escobar, bronze, 7'7''

Signed r. side of cane Marisol 1968

Hall of Columns

Born Joseph de Veuster in Tremeloo, Belgium. Became a member of the Congregation of the Sacred Hearts, given the name Damien. Missionary to Hawaii and ordained a Priest shortly after his arrival in 1864. Went to the leper colony on the island of Molokai in 1873 where he lived, labored and died of leprosy after 16 years devoted to improving the conditions in the colony. Often referred to as the Martyr of Molokai.

NEG. NO. 35033

NEG. NO. 35035

Jefferson Davis, 1808–1889, Mississippi
Signed r. base Augustus Lukeman, Sc. 1928;
    bronze, 7′7″
Statuary Hall

   Soldier, statesman, President of the Confederacy. A graduate of West Point; fought in the Black Hawk War, 1830–31; the War with Mexico. As Secretary of War under President Pierce 1853–57 he had jurisdiction over the erection of the new House and Senate wings and dome of the U.S. Capitol. U.S. House of Representatives 1845–46; U.S. Senator 1847–51, 1857–61. Elected President of the Southern Confederacy 1862.

Robert Fulton, 1765–1815, Pennsylvania
Signed front base Howard Roberts, Philada.,
    1883; marble, 5′4″
Statuary Hall

   Artist, civil engineer, inventor. Artist of merit and an experimenter in submarine mines and torpedoes; painted the first panorama ever shown in Paris. Achieved great distinction for the adaptation of steam power as a means of naval propulsion and for the design of the first successful steamboat, the *Clermont*.

240

NEG. NO. 35037

NEG. NO. 35038

JAMES ABRAM GARFIELD, 1831–1881, Ohio
Charles H. Niehaus, 1884-85 marble, 7′7″
Signed l. base Niehaus, sculptor
Rotunda

Soldier, lawyer, educator, statesman and President of
the U.S. Professor and later President of Hiram College,
1857–1861; member of the State senate 1859; Major
General in the Union Army, Civil War; Member of the
U.S. House of Representatives 1863–80; President 1881;
assassinated 5 months after his inauguration.

JAMES Z. GEORGE, 1826–1897, Mississippi
Signed r. base Augustus Lukeman, Sc., 1928;
    bronze, 7′8″
Hall of Columns

Lawyer, soldier in the War with Mexico and Confederate Brigadier General of the Civil War. Attained distinction as chief justice of the State supreme court 1879 and
as a U.S. Senator 1881–97; a leading member of the
Mississippi constitutional convention in 1890.

241

NEG. NO. 35039

NEG. NO. 27494

GEORGE WASHINGTON GLICK, 1827–1911, Kansas
Charles H. Niehaus, 1913–14, marble, 7'5''
Signed r. base C. H. Niehaus
Hall of Columns

JOHN GORRIE, 1803–1855, Florida
C. Adrian Pillars, marble, 7'6''
Signed r. base C. A. Pillars, 1913
Statuary Hall

Lawyer, farmer, statesman and Governor of Kansas. A soldier in the Union Army in the Civil War; served 14 years in the State legislature. He was an uncompromising free-State man, and helped to prepare the constitution upon which the State of Kansas was admitted to the Union.

Eminent physician and held the first patent on mechanical refrigeration which he developed to alleviate the suffering of the sick. This later led to discoveries of air conditioning and mechanical ice-making.

NEG. NO. 27451

NEG. NO. 35040

NATHANAEL GREENE, 1742–1786, Rhode Island
Henry Kirke Brown, marble, 6′4″
Signed top r. base H. K. Brown, 1869
East Central Hall

Deputy, General Assembly 1770–72, 1775; Major General 1776 in the Revolutionary War; was engaged in many major campaigns; acclaimed the "Savior of the South". His was the first statue to be placed in Statuary Hall 1870.

JOHN CAMPBELL GREENWAY, 1872–1926, Arizona
Signed top base Gutzon Borglum, 1928; bronze, 8′2″
Statuary Hall

Distinguished soldier in the War with Spain; a member of the Rough Riders; served in World War I with distinction; commissioned Brigadier General in 1922; noted mining engineer and inventor of the turbo log washer.

243

NEG. NO. 35041

NEG. NO. 27434

Hannibal Hamlin, 1809–1891, Maine
Signed top base Charles E. Tefft, 1933; bronze,
6'8"

Statuary Hall

Statesman, U.S. House of Representatives 1843–47;
U.S. Senate 1848–57, and resigned to become Governor
of Maine 1857. Reelected to U.S. Senate 1857–61;
elected Vice President under Lincoln 1861–65. Enlisted
as private in the Maine State Guard, Civil War 1864;
collector of port of Boston; U.S. Senate 1869–81; U.S.
Minister to Spain 1881–82, when he resigned to devote
the remainder of his life to agricultural pursuits.

Wade Hampton, 1818–1902, South Carolina
Frederic W. Ruckstull, marble, 7'6"
Signed r. base F. W. RUCKSTULL· FECIT·
1929·

House connecting corridor

Soldier, statesman, lawyer, Governor. Member of the
State senate 1858–62; served in the Confederate Army
commanding "Hampton's Legion"; rose to rank of
Lieutenant General commanded the Cavalry of the
Army of Northern Virginia; Governor of South Carolina
1876–79; and U.S. Senator 1879–91.

NEG. NO. 35042

JOHN HANSON, 1715–1783, Maryland
Signed l. base Richard E. Brooks, Sc., Paris
MCMII [1902]; bronze, 7'9''
Senate connecting corridor

Patriot and statesman; first President under the Articles
of Confederation; patriot of the Revolution; member of
State house of delegates 9 terms; member of State senate
1757–73; delegate to General Congress in Annapolis
1774; member of the Continental Congress 1780–83;
signer of the Articles of Confederation 1781.

NEG. NO. 35043

JAMES HARLAN, 1820–1899, Iowa
Nellie V. Walker, bronze, 8'4''
Signed l. base N. V. Walker, 1909
Hall of Columns

Distinguished statesman, educator and orator. Princi-
pal of Iowa City College; State Superintendent of Public
Instruction; President of Iowa Wesleyan College 1853–
55. Secretary of the Interior 1865–66 under Andrew
Johnson; U.S. Senator 1855–73; presiding judge on the
Alabama Claims Commission. His daughter married
Robert Todd Lincoln.

NEG. NO. 35044

SAMUEL HOUSTON, 1793–1863, Texas
Signed l. base Elisabet Ney, fec., Austin,
  Texas, 1904; marble, 6'10"
Statuary Hall

Soldier, statesman, Governor. Served in the Creek
War 1818; commander in chief of the Texas Army.
Lawyer, district attorney and adjutant general of Tenn.
1820; U.S. House of Representatives from Tenn. 1823–
27; Governor of Tenn. 1827–29; first President of Republic of Texas 1841–44; took first steps toward annexation of Texas; Senator from Texas 1856–59;
Governor of Texas 1859–61; deposed when he refused
to take the oath of allegiance to the Confederate States.

NEG. NO. 35046

JOHN J. INGALLS, 1833–1900, Kansas
Charles H. Niehaus, 1903–04 marble, 7'5"
Signed r. base C. H. Niehaus
Statuary Hall

Lawyer, scholar, orator and statesman. Delegate to
the Kansas constitutional convention; secretary of the
Kansas Territorial Council; member of the State
senate; secretary of state and served as judge advocate
during the Civil War, rising to the rank of lieutenant
colonel. Member of the U.S. Senate 1873–91.

NEG. NO. 35047

NEG. NO. 35048

ANDREW JACKSON, 1767–1845, Tennessee
Signed back of base Belle Kinney — L— F—
   Scholz, New York 1927; bronze, 7′6″
Rotunda

Lawyer, judge, soldier and 7th President of the U.S.
Courier in the Revolution at age 13; U.S. Representative
1796–97; Judge of Tenn. Supreme Court 1798–1804;
Creek War 1813; led the defeat of the British at New
Orleans 1815; captured Florida 1817 and became its
Governor 1821; U.S. Senate 1823–25; President 1829–37.

KING KAMEHAMEHA I, c. 1758–1819, Hawaii
Thomas R. Gould, bronze, 8′7″
Signed back of base T. R. Gould, Inv. Et. Fecit,
   Florence 1879. Cast in 1968 from the original
Statuary Hall

Beloved leader who became King by virtue of his
ability to unite the warring islands under one government. Ruled wisely and well 1782–1819, encouraged
peaceful activities of agriculture and fishing and engaged in brisk trade from the time of Capt. Cook's
visit. The flag design he ordered for his kingdom has
become the symbol of the State of Hawaii.

247

NEG. NO. 35049

NEG. NO. 28004

PHILIP KEARNY, 1814–1862, New Jersey
Henry Kirke Brown, bronze, 6′6″
Signed r. base H. K. Brown, Sculpt 1873
Hall of Columns

"The Perfect Soldier" who was distinguished on two continents for his conspicuous bravery and military accomplishments. He fought in Algiers 1840; in the War with Mexico 1848; and was Major General in the Civil War. He lost his life at Chantilly, Virginia, 1862.

JOHN E. KENNA, 1848–1893, West Virginia
Alexander Doyle, executed 1897–1901, marble
7′8″
Hall of Columns

Soldier, lawyer, statesman, enlisted in the Confederate Army in 1864 and was wounded in action; elected prosecuting attorney Kanawha County, 1872–1877; judge pro tem, circuit court of his home county, 1875; Member of the U.S. House of Representatives, 1877–1883; U.S. Senator 1883 until his death.

NEG. NO. 35050

THOMAS STARR KING, 1824–1864, California
Signed front base Haig Patigian, 1930; bronze,
7′2″
Hall of Columns

Preacher, patriot, orator; ordained a minister when 22 years old; received a call in 1860 to the First Unitarian Church of California. During his 4 years service in San Francisco he was a dominant factor in the support of the Union. His portrait hangs in the capitol at Sacramento. It bears this inscription:

"The man whose matchless oratory saved California to the Union."

NEG. NO. 27441

WILLIAM KING, 1768–1852, Maine
Signed r. base Franklin Simmons, Fecit 1877;
marble, 7′5″
House connecting corridor

Statesman, Governor, industrialist. Member of the Massachusetts legislature; assisted in securing passage of the Act of Toleration and the Betterment Act (the first step toward religious enfranchisement); Major General of the Maine Militia in the War of 1812. Leader in separating Maine from Massachusetts; President of Maine constitutional convention, 1819; elected first Governor of Maine in 1820.

NEG. NO. 35051

NEG. NO. 35052

FATHER EUSEBIO FRANCISCO KINO, S.J., 1645–
1711, Arizona

Signed l. base Suzanne Silvercruys 1964; bronze,
7′8″

Hall of Columns

A native of Italy and a contemporary of LaSalle and
Marquette; spent over 30 years in the Southwest as a
Jesuit missionary, explorer, cartographer, astronomer,
builder, historian and agriculturist; founded a chain of
24 missions and 19 ranches and made 14 expeditions into
the land which is now Arizona; began the cattle industry
in 3 places, planted fruit trees and introduced new grains.

SAMUEL JORDAN KIRKWOOD, 1813–1894, Iowa

Signed r. base Vinnie Ream; executed 1913,
bronze, 7′4″

Statuary Hall

Lawyer by profession, served as county prosecuting
attorney, 1845–49; member of the Ohio constitutional
convention, 1850–51; Iowa State senate, 1856–59;
Governor, 1860–64, 1876–77; U.S. Senator, 1866–67,
1877–81; Secretary of the Interior under President
Garfield, 1881–82.

250

NEG. NO. 35033

ROBERT M. LA FOLLETTE, SR., 1855–1925,
  Wisconsin

Signed r. base Jo Davidson 1928; marble, 6'6''
Statuary Hall

Lawyer, statesman, Governor; was district attorney,
Dane County, 1880–84; Member of the United States
House of Representatives, 1885–1891; Governor of
Wisconsin, 1901–1906; resigned on election to the
United States Senate where he served from 1906 until his
death in 1925. He wrote into the law of the land many
constructive measures designed to safeguard the liberties
and economic interest of the workers.

NEG. NO. 35054

REVEREND JASON LEE, 1803–1845, Oregon
Gifford MacG. Proctor, bronze, 6'11''
Signed l. back top of base G. MacG. Proctor 1952
Statuary Hall

Educator, missionary; orphaned at 3, self-supporting
at 13; educated in Mass. for the ministry; became the
first missionary in Oregon territory 1834; petitioned
Congress in 1838 to "take formal and speedy possession"
of the Oregon country.

251

NEG. NO. 35055

NEG. NO. 35056

ROBERT R. LIVINGSTON, 1746–1813, New York
Erastus Dow Palmer, bronze, 6'4''
Signed r. base E. D. Palmer, Sc., 1874
East Central Hall

ROBERT E. LEE, 1807–1870, Virginia
Signed l. base Edward V. Valentine, Sc.;
   executed 1909, bronze, 6'6''
Statuary Hall

A graduate of West Point, 1829 and superintendent, 1852, famed Confederate General of the Civil War. Following his heroic surrender to General Grant at Appomattox, he became President of Washington College at Lexington, Virginia, now named Washington and Lee University in his honor. He also served in the War with Mexico, 1847.

Jurist, diplomat, statesman. Delegate to the Continental Congress, 1775–77, 1779–81; one of committee of 5 who drafted the Declaration of Independence, but did not sign it; Delegate to State Constitutional Convention, 1777; Secretary of Foreign Affairs under the Articles of Confederation. As Chancellor of N.Y. State, he administered the first Presidential oath of office to George Washington, 1789; U.S. Minister to France, 1801–04, aided in negotiating the Louisiana Purchase; assisted Robert Fulton and his partner in constructing the first steamboat.

252

NEG. NO. 27496

DR. CRAWFORD WILLIAMSON LONG, 1815–1878, Georgia

J. Massey Rhind, 1924–25, marble, 7'2"

Signed front base Massey Rhind, Sc.

East Central Hall

Physician, humanitarian; first surgeon to use sulphuric ether as an anesthesia in 1842, considered one of the great events in the history of surgery.

NEG. NO. 35057

HUEY PIERCE LONG, 1893–1935, Louisiana

Signed r. back top Charles Keck, Sc.; executed 1938–40, bronze, 6'8"

Statuary Hall

Lawyer, State railroad commissioner; Governor of La., 1928–1932; U.S. Senator, 1932–1935. He fostered the distribution of free school books and equalized educational opportunities throughout Louisiana.

NEG. NO. 27452

NEG. NO. 35058

PERE JACQUES MARQUETTE, 1637–1675,
Wisconsin

Gaetano Trentanove, marble, 7′7″

Signed r. base Prof. G. Trentanove, Sculptor,
Florence, Italy; executed 1895

House connecting corridor

Pioneer explorer and missionary; French Jesuit missionary priest among the Indians of the northern country;
his missions at Sault Ste. Marie and Mackinaw became
the first towns in Michigan; explored the Miss. River and
died on the return trip in 1675. Because he was neither
a native nor a citizen of Wisconsin, the right of that State
to commemorate him was established by a joint resolution of Congress Oct. 21, 1893.

PATRICK ANTHONY MCCARRAN, 1876–1954
Nevada

Signed r. back top of base Yolande Jacobson,
1959; bronze, 7′3″

Statuary Hall vestibule north

Distinguished lawyer and statesman whose opinions as
Chief Justice of the Nevada supreme court, 1917–1918,
remain valued legal text; elected to the U.S. Senate in
1932, and served until his death in 1954.

254

NEG. NO. 35059

NEG. NO. 35060

Dr. Ephraim McDowell, 1771–1830, Kentucky
Charles H. Niehaus, bronze, 7'4''
Signed r. base C. H. Niehaus, Sculptor, 1928
Senate connecting corridor

A renowned physician, attended the University of
Edinburgh, Scotland; successfully performed the first
operation known as Ovariotomy in 1809; one of the
founders and original trustees of Centre College, Dan-
ville, Kentucky; and a member of many medical
societies.

Dr. John McLoughlin, 1784–1857, Oregon
Signed top base Gifford Proctor, Sc., 1952;
    bronze, 6'11''
House connecting corridor

Often called "the Father of Oregon"; was head of the
powerful Hudson's Bay Company in the Pacific Northwest territory, 1824–1845; assisted the missionaries and
settlers in what is now Washington and Oregon. His
mild and just paternalistic rule aided the pioneers of the
region to govern themselves and pass peacefully from
British rule to American territorial status.

255

NEG. NO. 35061

NEG. NO. 35062

ESTHER HOBART MORRIS, 1813/14–1902, Wyoming
Signed l. base Avard Fairbanks, 1958; bronze, 8'
Statuary Hall vestibule north

Judge; mother of woman suffrage in Wyoming, was a convincing proponent and advocate of laws granting voting and office holding privileges to the women of the Wyoming territory; first woman to hold the office of justice of the peace, and no decision of hers was ever reversed by appeal to a higher court.

J. STERLING MORTON, 1832–1902, Nebraska
Rudulph Evans, 1936–37, bronze, 6'9"
Signed r. base R. Evans, Sc
Hall of Columns

A prominent statesman; leader in the early history of Nebraska; Secretary of the Nebraska Territory and acting Governor, 1858–1859; Secretary of Agriculture under President Cleveland, 1893, and originator of Arbor Day.

NEG. NO. 27522

NEG. NO. 35063

John Peter Gabriel Muhlenberg, 1746–1807
  Pennsylvania
Signed l. base Blanche Nevin, 1884; marble,
  6'6"
Small House rotunda

Soldier, clergyman, statesman. Clergyman in Lutheran and Episcopal churches; member of Virginia House of Burgesses, 1774; Major General in Revolutionary War; Vice President of Pennsylvania Supreme Executive Council, 1785–1787; member of Pennsylvania constitutional convention 1790; member of U.S. House of Representatives, 1789–1791; 1793–1795; 1799–1801; member of U.S. Senate, 1801; Supervisor of Revenue for Pennsylvania, 1801; collector of Customs, 1802.

Oliver P. Morton, 1823–1877, Indiana
Charles H. Niehaus, 1897–99, marble, 7'6"
Signed l. base Niehaus, Sculptor
Hall of Columns

Served as circuit court judge, Indiana; Lt. Governor; Civil War governor who supported Lincoln and the Union cause; member of the U.S. Senate, 1867–77.

NEG. NO. 35064

NEG. NO. 35065

FRANCIS H. PIERPONT, 1814–1899, West Virginia
Signed l. base Franklin Simmons, 1903; marble,
   7'7''

Statuary Hall

   Patriot, statesman, Governor. Chosen Provisional
Governor of Virginia in 1861 by a staunch Union convention when state officials declared support for the
Confederacy; served as elected Governor of Virginia
1863–68; led the severance movement in western Virginia which resulted in the creation of West Virginia as
an independent state in 1863.

HENRY MOWER RICE, 1817–1894, Minnesota
Frederick E. Triebel, 1913–16, marble, 7'7''
Signed r. base Prof. F. E. Triebel, Sculptor,
   College Point, New York
Statuary Hall

   Businessman, statesman; was instrumental in securing
Minnesota Statehood; a delegate from the Territory;
later U.S. Senator 1853–63; appointed U.S. Commissioner to negotiate Indian Treaties, 1887–88.

NEG. NO. 35066

Caesar Rodney, 1728–1784, Delaware
Signed r. base Bryant Baker, Sc., 1932; marble,
    7'5"
East Central Hall

Patriot, jurist; Delegate to the Stamp Act Congress;
signer of the Declaration of Independence; a Member of
the Continental Congress; Major General in the Revolutionary War; was in command at the Battle of Trenton;
President of Delaware, 1778–1782; and occupied many
positions of note in his native State.

NEG. NO. 35067

Will Rogers, 1879–1935, Oklahoma
Signed r. base Jo Davidson, Paris, 1938; bronze,
    7'6"
House connecting corridor

Humorist, humanitarian, cowboy, showman, come-
dian (stage, screen, and radio), actor, author, after-
dinner speaker, columnist, commentator, philosopher,
world traveler, goodwill ambassador.

259

NEG. NO. 23357

NEG. NO. 35068

URIAH M. ROSE, 1834–1913, Arkansas
Frederic W. Ruckstuhl, marble, 7′6″
Signed r. base F. W. Ruckstuhl, Fecit, 1917
Statuary Hall

Lawyer of international reputation; chancellor of the State; charter member of American Bar Association and its president in 1901; authored the "Arkansas Constitution" and "Digest of Arkansas Reports"; appointed by Theodore Roosevelt in 1907 as one of the delegates to the Peace Congress of The Hague with the rank of ambassador.

CHARLES MARION RUSSELL, 1864–1926, Montana
John B. Weaver, 1957–58, bronze, 7′1″
Signed back of base Jack Weaver, Sculptor
Statuary Hall

Known as "The Cowboy Artist," was an illustrator, writer, philosopher, and humorist who faithfully and devotedly recorded the spirit of the Old West.

260

NEG. NO. 35069

DR. FLORENCE RENA SABIN, 1871–1953, Colorado
Signed l. side of chair Joy Flinsch Buba 1958;
 bronze, 5'3''
Statuary Hall

Distinguished teacher, scientist, humanitarian and
writer of medical texts; pioneered woman membership
into the National Academy of Sciences and entrance
into Johns Hopkins Medical School; faculty member of
the Rockefeller Institute of Medical Research; she was
instrumental in the drafting and enacting of the *Sabin
Health Laws* in Colorado.

NEG. NO. 35070

MARIA L. SANFORD, 1836–1920, Minnesota
Signed l. base Evelyn Raymond 1958; bronze,
 6'11''
Senate connecting corridor

Noted woman orator and educator—one of the first
women professors in the U.S.; leader in adult education;
founder of early parent-teacher groups; espoused
education for Negroes, justice for the Indians, and
women's rights.

NEG. NO. 35071

NEG. NO. 35072

SEQUOYA, 1770–1845, Oklahoma
Signed r. base Vinnie Ream/G. J. Zolnay;
   executed 1917, bronze, 7'6''
Statuary Hall

   Cherokee leader, skilled as a silversmith, blacksmith, philosopher, trader, but famous because he developed the 86 character alphabet for the Cherokee Nation 1821, thus giving his people a written language. Sent to Washington as a delegate from Western Cherokees 1828; Anglicized name was George Guess.

JUNIPERO SERRA, 1713–1784, California
Ettore Cadorin, 1930, bronze, 8'9''
Signed r. base E. Cadorin
Statuary Hall

   Missionary, pioneer of pioneers; founder and moving spirit of 9 California missions between 1769–84, during his presidency of the Franciscan friars.

262

NEG. NO. 35073

NEG. NO. 35074

JOHN SEVIER, 1745–1815, Tennessee
Belle Kinney Scholz and Leopold F. Scholz,
   bronze, 7′10″, executed 1931
Signed l. base Belle Kinney/L. F. Scholz, SCˢ
Statuary Hall

Soldier, statesman, frontier leader; Capt. of Colonial
Militia 1773–74; county and district judge 1777–80;
served in the Revolution; Governor of the proclaimed
"State of Franklin" 1785–88; first Governor of Tennessee
1796–1801 and 1803–09; U.S. House of Representatives
from North Carolina 1789–91; returned to the House
1811 as a member from Tennessee and served until his
death.

ROGER SHERMAN, 1721–1793, Connecticut
Chauncey B. Ives, marble, 7′11″
Signed r. base C. B. Ives, Fecit, Romae, 1870
East Central Hall

The only member of the Continental Congress to sign
the Declaration of 1774, the Declaration of Independence, the Articles of Confederation, and the Federal
Constitution. He served in the Connecticut legislature,
the Continental Congress, the Constitutional Convention,
the U.S. House of Representatives, 1789–91, and the
U.S. Senate, 1791–93.

263

NEG. NO. 35075

NEG. NO. 27852

GENERAL JAMES SHIELDS, 1810–1879, Illinois
Signed r. base Leonard W. Volk, Sculptor, 1893;
 bronze, 7'6''
Hall of Columns

State supreme court justice; a brigadier general in the War with Mexico, 1846–48; a Union officer in the Civil War, 1861–63; appointed Governor of the Oregon Territory by President Polk; U.S. Senator from 3 States—Illinois, 1849–55, Minnesota, 1858–59, and Missouri, 1879.

GEORGE L. SHOUP, 1836–1904, Idaho
Frederick E. Triebel, marble, 7'7''
Signed back of base Prof. F. E. Triebel, Sculptor,
 New York, 1909
Statuary Hall

Pioneer, soldier and statesman; delegate to the Colorado Territorial constitutional convention 1864; colonel in the Union Army in the Civil War; Governor of the Idaho Territory, 1889–90; elected first Governor of Idaho, 1890; resigned to become first U.S. Senator from Idaho, 1890–1901.

NEG. NO. 35076

NEG. NO. 27453

GENERAL EDMUND KIRBY SMITH, 1824–1893, Florida

Charles A. Pillars, bronze, 7'5''

Signed r. base C. A. Pillars, SC. 1917

Hall of Columns

Soldier-educator; graduated with honors from West Point, served in the War with Mexico and was a General in the Confederate Army; Chancellor of the University of Nashville; taught mathematics at West Point, 1849–52, and the University of Sewanee (Tenn.).

JOHN STARK, 1728–1822, New Hampshire

Carl Conrads, 1894, marble, 6'5''

Vestibule north of Rotunda

Patriot and soldier; a courageous and relentless soldier during the French and Indian War, 1754–1763; led Washington's advance at Trenton, 1776; headed the New Hampshire troops at the Battle of Bunker Hill, 1775; and won the Battle of Bennington, 1777; commissioned a Major General in 1786.

NEG. NO. 35077

ALEXANDER HAMILTON STEPHENS, 1812–1883,
    Georgia
Gutzon Borglum, marble 5'8'', executed 1926–
    27
Statuary Hall

Lawyer, U.S. Representative 1843–59; elected to the
Confederate Congress and chosen vice president of the
provisional government of the Confederacy, 1861–65;
was elected to the U.S. Senate after the war but was
denied admission; author of *The War Between the States;*
U.S. House of Representatives, 1873–82; Governor of
Georgia, 1882–83.

NEG. NO. 35078

RICHARD STOCKTON, 1730–1781, New Jersey
Henry Kirke Brown, marble, 6'3''
Signed front base H. K. Brown, 1874
East Central Hall

Lawyer, jurist and signer of the Declaration of
Independence; an associate justice on the New Jersey
supreme court, 1774–1776; a member of the Continental
Congress, 1776.

266

NEG. NO. 27436

NEG. NO. 35080

JONATHAN TRUMBULL, 1710–1785, Connecticut
Chauncey B. Ives, marble, 8'1''
Signed r. base C. B. Ives, Fecit, Romae, 1869
House connecting corridor

Soldier, statesman and minister; espoused the cause of independence, aided General Washington, and worked for a stronger Union; one of the outstanding figures of Connecticut commerce, served in the Connecticut Assembly; Governor 15 years; State's chief justice in colonial times, 1769–1784; father of the artist John Trumbull.

ZEBULON BAIRD VANCE, 1830–1894, North Carolina
Signed top base Gutzon Borglum, 1916; bronze, 7'8''
Statuary Hall

Soldier, lawyer, statesman. Member of the State house of commons, 1854; Member of the U.S. House of Representatives, 1858–1861; entered the Confederate Army during the Civil War as a captain, 1861; promoted to a Colonel; twice Governor of North Carolina, served in the U.S. Senate, 1879–1894.

NEG. NO. 35081

NEG. NO. 35082

JOSEPH WARD, 1838–1889, South Dakota
Signed r. base Bruno Beghé, Sculptor; executed
  1963, marble, 7'2''
Hall of Columns

Educator, churchman, and statesman; organized Yankton Academy, 1872; founded Yankton College, 1881; drafted a code of school laws for the Dakota Territory; served in the Union Army; ordained a missionary, 1869; the "father of Congregationalism" in the Dakotas. Outstanding leader in the struggle for South Dakota Statehood; author of State Constitution as adopted; composed the state motto, "Under God the people rule," and the Great Seal of South Dakota is the result for his written description for this emblem.

GENERAL LEW WALLACE, 1827–1905, Indiana
Andrew O'Connor, marble, 6'10'', executed
  1908–09
Signed r. base A. O'Connor
Statuary Hall

Successful as lawyer, soldier, diplomat, and author; served in the War with Mexico; Major General during the Civil War; served in the Indiana State senate, as territorial Governor of New Mexico and Minister to Turkey; authored the classic novel, *Ben Hur* one of the best sellers of all time.

268

NEG. NO. 35083

NEG. NO. 35084

GEORGE WASHINGTON, 1732–1799, Virginia
Antoine Houdon, bronze, 7′6″; 1909 casting
  from the original 1788 marble
Rotunda

Statesman, patriot, soldier, surveyor, first President of the United States; commander in chief of the Colonial forces; President of the Constitutional Convention; delegate to the First and Second Constitutional Congresses.

DANIEL WEBSTER, 1782–1852, New Hampshire
Carl Conrads, executed 1893–94, marble, 6′4″
Statuary Hall

Constitutional lawyer, orator and statesman; Represented his native State, New Hampshire in the U.S. House of Representatives, 1813–1817; represented his adopted State of Massachusetts in the House, 1823–1827 and in the U.S. Senate, 1827–1841 and 1845–1850. Secretary of State under Presidents Harrison, Tyler and Fillmore.

NEG. NO. 35085

NEG. NO. 35086

GENERAL JOSEPH WHEELER, 1836–1906, Alabama

Berthold Nebel, executed 1923–25, bronze, 7′
Signed l. back top of base B. Nebel
Statuary Hall

Soldier, lawyer, graduate of West Point, served in the Confederate Army and attained the rank of senior cavalry officer; served in the Army during the War with Spain and was made brigadier general; a Representative in Congress eighteen years.

EDWARD DOUGLASS WHITE, 1845–1921, Louisiana

Signed top r. side of base Arthur Morgan, Sculptor, 1954; bronze, 7′1″
Senate connecting corridor

Noted jurist, and statesman; at 16 he became a soldier in the Confederate Army; Member of State senate, 1874–1878; associate justice of the State supreme court, 1879–1880; elected U.S. Senator, 1891–1894; appointed Associate Justice of the Supreme Court of the U.S., 1894; Chief Justice of the U.S., 1910–1921.

NEG. NO. 35087

NEG. NO. 35088

MARCUS WHITMAN, 1802–1847, Washington
Signed l. base Avard Fairbanks, 1950; bronze,
9'
Statuary Hall

Pioneer, doctor, missionary, farmer; courageous medical missionary in the Washington Territory; in 1836 he led a party to the Oregon Territory and settled near the present city of Walla Walla, Washington; assisted the "Great Emigration" of 1843, the first large movement of settlers to the northwest. He and his wife Narcissa, were massacred by the Indians in 1847.

FRANCES E. WILLARD, 1839–1898, Illinois
Signed l. base Helen Farnsworth Mears,
Fecit, MCMV [1905]; marble, 7'1''
Statuary Hall

Educator, social and economic reformer, orator and journalist; president of Evanston College for Ladies, 1871 (later part of Northwestern University); dean and professor of aesthetics at Northwestern; associated in evangelist movement with Dwight Moody, 1873; elected president of National Woman's Temperance Union, 1879; founder and president of World's Christian Temperance Union, 1883.

271

NEG. NO. 35089

NEG. NO. 35090

ROGER WILLIAMS, 1603–1682/83, Rhode Island
Signed l. base Franklin Simmons, Sculptor,
   Rome, 1870; marble, 6′8″
Hall of Columns

Colonizer, minister, founder of Rhode Island. Born
in England, came to America, 1631; pastor of the
Puritan Church at Salem, Mass. Banished from the
Massachusetts colony in 1635: founded Rhode Island,
1636, and secured the charter for the Providence
Plantations, 1644; author of the great declaration of the
principle of religious liberty and freedom in the organization of the State; his statue was the second to be
placed in Statuary Hall, 1872.

JOHN WINTHROP, 1588–1649, Massachusetts
Signed l. base Richard S. Greenough, Sculpsit,
   1875; marble, 7′8″
Hall of Columns

Puritan colonizer, author, lawyer; first Governor of
Massachusetts Bay Colony, and served 12 years; believed
in evangelizing the Indians; opposed democracy, and
believed superior minds, though always in the minority,
should rule.

NEG. NO. 35091

BRIGHAM YOUNG, 1801–1877, Utah
Mahonri Young, marble, 5′11″
Signed r. base Mahonri, 1947
Statuary Hall

Pioneer, empire builder; led the Mormon pioneers to Salt Lake Valley in 1847; preeminent in the settling and establishing of the Territory of Deseret, now the State of Utah; and was one of the Territory's most illustrious Governors; President of The Church of Jesus Christ of Latter-day Saints 1844–1877.

273

# STATUES NOT CONTRIBUTED BY STATES

NINE STATUES

NEG. NO. 35092

NEG. NO. 26687

EDWARD DICKINSON BAKER, 1811–1861
Horatio Stone, marble, 6'5''
Purchase authorized 1873, Stats. L., v. 17, p. 513
Rotunda

U.S. Representative from Illinois 1845–46; served in Mexican and Civil Wars; Senator from Oregon from 1860 until October 21, 1861, when he was killed at Balls Bluff, Virginia, while serving as a major general in the Union Army.

BENJAMIN FRANKLIN, 1706–1790
Signed r. base H. Powers, Sculp, 1862; marble, 7'11''
Contract for purchase 1859; placed 1862
Senate wing, second floor, east corridor

NEG. NO. 35094                         NEG. NO. 35096

GENERAL ULYSSES S. GRANT, 1822–1885
Signed l. base Franklin Simmons, Fecit 1899;
   marble, 7'5''
Gift from Grand Army of the Republic, 1890
Accepted by Public Res. 39, 51st Congress
Rotunda

ALEXANDER HAMILTON, 1757–1804
Signed r. base Horatio Stone, Fac Rome 1868;
   marble, 7'9''
Purchased 1866–68; placed 1868
Rotunda

NEG. NO. 26688

NEG. NO. 35098

THOMAS JEFFERSON, 1743–1826
Signed r. base P. J. David D'angers, Sculp. 1833;
    bronze, 7'6''
Gift of Lt. Uriah P. Levy USN, 1833
Rotunda

By resolution placed in Rotunda 1834 for about a
year, then moved to the north grounds of the White
House; returned to the Capitol in 1874 and formally
accepted by resolution of March 18, 1874.

JOHN HANCOCK, 1737–1793
Signed r. base Horatio Stone, Sculp't 1861;
    marble, 7'6''
Purchased 1857–61
Senate wing, second floor, west corridor

276

NEG. NO. 26348

NEG. NO. 35099

THOMAS JEFFERSON, 1743–1826
Signed l. side of column H. Powers, Sculp
    1863; marble, 8′
Purchased by contract 1859; placed 1863
House wing, second floor, east corridor

ABRAHAM LINCOLN, 1809–1865
Signed r. base Vinnie Ream, 1870; marble, 6′
    11″
Purchased 1871
Rotunda

277

NEG. NO. 35100

SAM RAYBURN, 1882–1961
Signed top r. base Felix de Weldon, Sc. 1965; bronze, 6′
Gift of Texas State Society of Washington, D.C., 1965
Accepted by House Office Building Commission, 1964
Rayburn House Office Building, main entrance

Representative from Texas 1913–1961.

# STATUE OF LIBERTY AND THE EAGLE

In the niche above the entablature on the south wall of Statuary Hall stands the heroic-sized figure of Liberty. Placed there between 1817–1819 when the Capitol was rebuilt after the fire of 1814, she originally looked down on the House of Representatives which met in the Hall. Her right hand, extending over the American eagle, holds the Constitution of the United States. At her left is the frustum of a column serving as an altar around which the serpent, the emblem of wisdom, is entwined.

NEG. NO. 35101

LIBERTY AND THE EAGLE
Enrico Causici, plaster, 13'7''
Statuary Hall

279

# MEMORIAL TO THE PIONEERS OF THE WOMEN'S SUFFRAGE MOVEMENT

This portrait monument was accepted as a gift from the women of the United States, through the National Woman's Party, by the Joint Committee on the Library, February 15, 1921. The original block of marble from which these busts were carved measured 7′ x 5′ 8″ x 5′, and the estimated weight is between 7 and 8 tons.

In accepting the monument the Joint Committee on the Library directed that it be placed temporarily "in the Rotunda for the purpose of appropriate ceremonies of tender and reception and at the conclusion of the ceremonies, the said sculpture be placed in the Crypt on the first floor of the Capitol beneath the Dome." It was moved from the Rotunda to the Crypt May 1921.

NEG. NO. 33706

ELIZABETH CADY STANTON (1815–1902), 26″
Susan B. Anthony (1820–1906), 35″
Lucretia Mott (1793–1880), 24″
Signed r. side Adelaide Johnson, 1921; and l.r. on back A.J.
Crypt, first floor

# Reliefs

House Chamber
Old Supreme Court Chamber
Rotunda
Senate Chamber
East Central Portico

# RELIEFS IN THE HOUSE CHAMBER

## LAWGIVERS

The 23 relief portraits in marble are of men noted in history for the part they played in the evolution of what has become American law. They were placed over the gallery doors of the House of Representatives Chamber when it was remodeled 1949–50.

Created in bas relief of white Vermont marble by seven different sculptors, the plaques each measure 28″ in diameter. One is full face, and 22 are profile. From the full face of Moses on the north wall, 11 profiles face left and 11 face right, ending at the Webster quotation on the south wall above the Speaker's chair. (See page 398.)

The subjects of the plaques were jointly chosen by a group from the University of Pennsylvania, and the Columbia Historical Society of Washington, D.C. in consultation with authoritative staff members of the Library of Congress. The selection was approved by a special committee of five Members of the House of Representatives, the Architect of the Capitol and his associates.

The plaster models of these reliefs may be seen on the walls of the Rayburn House Office Building subway terminal.

In chronological order the lawgivers are:

| | | | |
|---|---|---|---|
| Hammurabi | c 2067–2025 B.C. | St. Louis | 1214–1270 A.D. |
| Moses | c 1571–1451 B.C. | Alphonso X | 1221–1284 A.D. |
| Lycurgus | c 900 B.C. | Edward I | 1239–1307 A.D. |
| Solon | c 594 B.C. | Suleiman | 1494–1566 A.D. |
| Gaius | c 110–180 A.D. | Grotius | 1583–1645 A.D. |
| Papinian | c 200 A.D. | Colbert | 1619–1683 A.D. |
| Justinian | c 483–565 A.D. | Pothier | 1699–1772 A.D. |
| Tribonian | c 500–547 A.D. | Blackstone | 1723–1780 A.D. |
| Maimonides | c 1135–1204 A.D. | Mason | 1726–1792 A.D. |
| Gregory IX | c 1147–1241 A.D. | Jefferson | 1743–1826 A.D. |
| Innocent III | 1161–1216 A.D. | Napoleon | 1769–1821 A.D. |
| de Montfort | 1200–1265 A.D. | | |

The accompanying illustrations are arranged alphabetically.

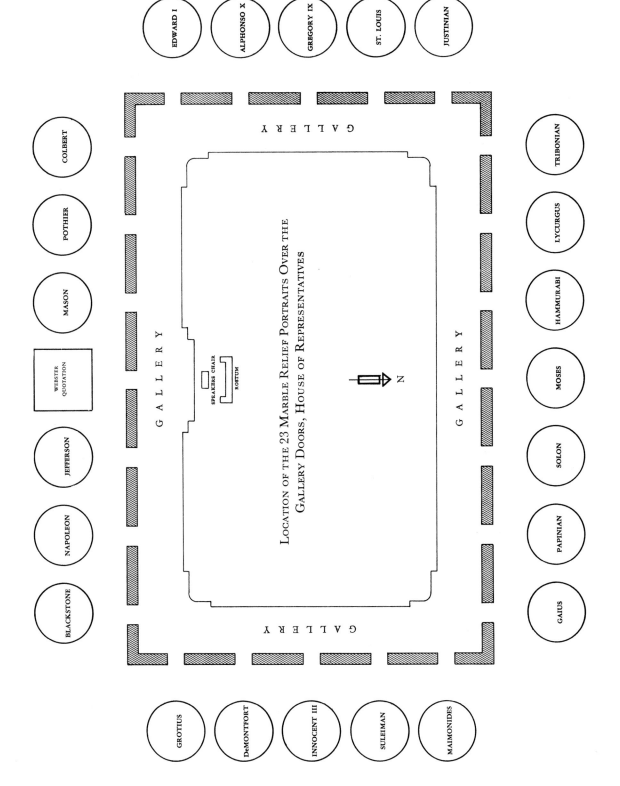

EDWARD I ALPHONSO X GREGORY IX ST. LOUIS JUSTINIAN

COLBERT

POTHIER

MASON

WEBSTER
QUOTATION

JEFFERSON

NAPOLEON

BLACKSTONE

TRIBONIAN

LYCURGUS

HAMMURABI

MOSES

SOLON

PAPINIAN

GAIUS

GALLERY

GALLERY

GALLERY

GALLERY

SPEAKERS CHAIR
ROSTUM

N

LOCATION OF THE 23 MARBLE RELIEF PORTRAITS OVER THE
GALLERY DOORS, HOUSE OF REPRESENTATIVES

GROTIUS DeMONTFORT INNOCENT III SULEIMAN MAIMONIDES

NEG. NO. 34061

ALPHONSO X, THE "WISE," 1221–1284
Gaetano Cecere
Signed l.r. G. Cecere

King of Leon and Castile; author of the *Fuero Real*, a compilation of local legislation for general use; originator of the code, *Las Siete Partidas*, used as a basis for Spanish jurisprudence.

NEG. NO. 34062

BLACKSTONE, 1723–1780
Thomas Hudson Jones
Signed l.r. T. H. Jones

Sir William Blackstone, celebrated English jurist; author of *Commentaries on the Laws of England*, which had considerable influence on the importation and adaptation of English common law in this country.

NEG. NO. 34063

COLBERT, 1619–1683
Laura Gardin Fraser
Signed l.r. L. G. F.

Jean Baptiste Colbert, French statesman; codifier of ordinances; reformer of the French legal system.

NEG. NO. 34064

DE MONTFORT, c. 1200–1265
Gaetano Cecere
Signed bottom center G. Cecere

Simon de Montfort, English statesman; advocate of representative government.

284

NEG. NO. 34065

EDWARD I
Laura Gardin Fraser
Signed l.r. L. G. F.

King of England; eliminator of feudalism from political life; summoner of the "Model Parliament," which established the parliamentary constitution of England.

NEG. NO. 34066

GAIUS, c. 110–180
Joseph Kiselewski

Celebrated Roman jurist; author of several works including the *Institutes*, a complete exposition of the elements of Roman law which became important sources of Roman civil law.

NEG. NO. 34067

GREGORY IX, c. 1147–1241
Thomas Hudson Jones
Signed l.r. T. H. Jones

Author of a compilation of decretals on canon law, who accomplished much in maintaining the remnants of Roman law during a critical period.

NEG. NO. 34068

GROTIUS, 1583–1645
C. Paul Jennewein

Hugo Grotius, Dutch statesman; Advocate-General of the provinces of Holland and Zeeland; author of *De jure qelli et pacis*, a fundamental doctrine of international law.

285

NEG. NO. 34069

HAMMURABI, reigned 2067–2025 B.C.
Thomas Hudson Jones
Signed l.r. T. H. Jones

King of Babylonia; author of a great law code bearing his name which is characterized by its primitiveness and recognized in legal literature as perhaps the earliest surviving code.

NEG. NO. 34070

INNOCENT III, 1161–1216
Joseph Kiselewski

Student of canon and civil law, who, like Gregory IX, preserved the remnants of Roman law during a dark and critical period of human history.

NEG. NO. 34071

JEFFERSON, 1743–1826
C. Paul Jennewein

Thomas Jefferson, third President of the United States; author of the Declaration of Independence and the Statute of Virginia for Religious Freedom.

NEG. NO. 34072

JUSTINIAN I, 483–565
Gaetano Cecere
Signed l.r. G. Cecere

Byzantine emperor who consolidated the pre-existing Roman law into two collections, the *Digest* or *Pandects* and the *Corpus Iuris Civilis*.

NEG. NO. 34073

LYCURGUS, c. 900 B.C.
C. Paul Jennewein

Legislator, traditional author of laws and institutions of Sparta.

NEG. NO. 34074

MAIMONIDES, 1135–1204
Brenda Putnam.

Jewish philosopher who compiled a systematic exposition of the whole of Jewish law as contained in the Pentateuch and in Talmudic literature.

NEG. NO. 34075

MASON, 1725–1792
Gaetano Cecere
Signed l.r. G. Cecere

George Mason, drafter of the Virginia Constitution and Bill of Rights 1776; member of the Constitutional Convention in 1787; originator of several amendments later incorporated in the present Bill of Rights.

NEG. NO. 34076

MOSES, c. 1571–1451 B.C.
Jean de Marco
Signed l.r. J. De Marco

Unexcelled Hebrew prophet and lawgiver who transformed an enslaved wandering people into a nation, disciplined and breathed into them character; received the Ten Commandments.

287

NEG. NO. 34077

Napoleon I, 1769–1821
C. Paul Jennewein
Signed l.l. C. P. Jennewein, Sc., 1950

Emperor of France who appointed a commission to draw up the *code civil*, a combination of tradition and Roman law which was quite influential on the legal systems of European and American states during the 19th century.

NEG. NO. 34087

Papinian, died c. 212
Laura Gardin Fraser

Roman jurist, remarkable for his juridical genius, independence of judgment, lucidity and firmness, and for his sense of right and morality by which he frequently rose above the barriers of national prejudices.

NEG. NO. 34079

Pothier, 1699–1772
Joseph Kiselewski

Robert Joseph Pothier, French jurist; author of *Pandectae Justinianae in novum ordinem digestae*, a classic in the study of Roman law; author of several treatises on French law, incorporated in the French Code Civil.

NEG. NO. 34080

Saint Louis, 1214–1270
Jean de Marco
Signed l.r. J. De Marco

(Louis IX) King of France; author of the *Mise of Amiens*.

288

NEG. NO. 34081

SOLON, c. 638–558 B.C.
Brenda Putnam

Athenian statesman; author of constitutional and legal reforms.

NEG. NO. 34082

SULEIMAN, 1494–1566
Joseph Kiselewski

Sultan of Turkey; reformed and improved civil and military codes and ameliorated the lot of his Christian subjects.

NEG. NO. 34083

Tribonian, c. 500–547
Signed bottom center: Brenda Putnam, Sc., 1950

Byzantine jurist; head of the commission which compiled the laws under Justinian I.

289

# STATE SEALS IN THE CEILING OF THE HOUSE OF REPRESENTATIVES

Upon the completion of the skylight of the chamber of the House of Representatives, stained glass seals of the 31 States and 4 possessions of the United States were installed in 1857–1858. These early seals were designed and painted by Johannes Adam Oertel. New seals were added as States were admitted to the Union, but the artists have not been documented.

During the remodeling of the House Chamber in 1949, the old cast iron ceiling with its glass skylights was replaced. The glass seals, which were about 21″ in diameter of double thick ornamental glass in iron frames, were given to the respective States.

New seals were reproduced from the original glass seals. They were cast in plaster and painted the appropriate colors.

In the center of the new ceiling there is a laylight, the field of which is of carved glass outlining the figure of an eagle, framed in bronze. It is illuminated artificially from above.

The seals of Hawaii and Alaska were added in 1962.

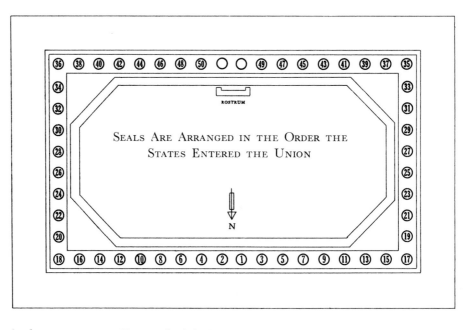

From the lower center reading to the left the seals are:

| | | | |
|---|---|---|---|
| 2 | Pennsylvania | 28 | Texas |
| 4 | Georgia | 30 | Wisconsin |
| 6 | Massachusetts | 32 | Minnesota |
| 8 | South Carolina | 34 | Kansas |
| 10 | Virginia | 36 | Nevada |
| 12 | North Carolina | 38 | Colorado |
| 14 | Vermont | 40 | South Dakota |
| 16 | Tennessee | 42 | Washington |
| 18 | Louisiana | 44 | Wyoming |
| 20 | Mississippi | 46 | Oklahoma |
| 22 | Alabama | 48 | Arizona |
| 24 | Missouri | 50 | Hawaii |
| 26 | Michigan | 0 | Virgin Islands |

From the lower center reading to the right the seals are:

| | | | |
|---|---|---|---|
| 1 | Delaware | 27 | Florida |
| 3 | New Jersey | 29 | Iowa |
| 5 | Connecticut | 31 | California |
| 7 | Maryland | 33 | Oregon |
| 9 | New Hampshire | 35 | West Virginia |
| 11 | New York | 37 | Nebraska |
| 13 | Rhode Island | 39 | North Dakota |
| 15 | Kentucky | 41 | Montana |
| 17 | Ohio | 43 | Idaho |
| 19 | Indiana | 45 | Utah |
| 21 | Illinois | 47 | New Mexico |
| 23 | Maine | 49 | Alaska |
| 25 | Arkansas | 0 | Puerto Rico |

# RELIEF IN OLD SUPREME COURT CHAMBER

## JUSTICE

This plaster relief is located in the chamber the Supreme Court used for 60 years. The appropriate relief of Justice was commissioned for the Court after the fire of 1814. A mythical figure of Justice is seated in the center of the lunette. In her left hand she holds the scales, and her right hand rests upon a sword. On the right is an eagle guarding the laws: on the left, a youthful winged figure—presumably typifying the Young Nation—crowned by the rising sun, is pointing to the Constitution of the United States. The background is light blue with accents of gold on the edges of the books, on the sun, the writing on the tablet, and on the scales.

NEG. NO. 40194

JUSTICE
Carlo Franzoni, plaster, May 1817
S–141

291

# RELIEFS IN THE ROTUNDA

Above each of the four Rotunda doors are scenes from the history of the American Colonies carved in relief into the sandstone walls. The three sculptors who decorated the Rotunda were employed during the rebuilding of the Capitol after the fire of 1814.

Between the historic scenes, decorative panels of wreaths and portraits, also in relief, circle the Rotunda walls.

NEG. NO. 24560

CONFLICT OF DANIEL BOONE AND THE INDIANS, 1773

Signed l.r. Enrico Causici of Verona, Fecit; 1826–27

Rotunda, above south door

NEG. NO. 24561

WILLIAM PENN'S TREATY WITH THE INDIANS, 1682

Nicholas Gevelot

Signed l.l. N. Gevelot, 1827

Rotunda, above north door

NEG. NO. 24559

LANDING OF THE PILGRIMS, 1620
Signed l.r. Enrico Causici of Verona, Fecit, 1825
Rotunda, above east door

NEG. NO. 24562

PRESERVATION OF CAPTAIN SMITH BY POCAHONTAS, 1606
Signed l.l. A. Capellano, Fecit, 1825
Rotunda, above west door

NEG. NO. 24566

JOHN CABOT
Francisco Iardella, 1828
Above the painting "Landing of Columbus"

NEG. NO. 24565

CHRISTOPHER COLUMBUS
Attributed to Francisco Iardella
Above the painting "Surrender of General Burgoyne"

NEG. NO. 24563

RENÉ ROBERT CAVELIER SIEUR DE LA SALLE
Francisco Iardella, 1829
Above the painting "Discovery of the Mississippi River"

NEG. NO. 24564

SIR WALTER RALEIGH
Attributed to Francisco Iardella
Above the painting "Surrender of Lord Cornwallis"

# RELIEFS IN THE SENATE CHAMBER

Three marble panels, designed by sculptor Lee Lawrie, were placed above the entries to the Senate Chamber when it was remodeled 1949–50.

The plaster models of these panels are located on the walls of the Capitol terminal of the Senate subway.

NEG. NO. 24722

COURAGE
Lee Lawrie
Bruno Mankowski, carver
West entry

Courage, symbolizing our Nation, unflinchingly battles Evil, the serpent, and vanquishes it.

NEG. NO. 24720

PATRIOTISM
Lee Lawrie
Louis Milione, carver
East entry

Patriotism is depicted by a citizen leaning on his plow, a symbol of every man's usual work, which he leaves to take up the sword for the defense of his country. The strident eagle symbolizes Vigilance and Preparedness.

NEG. NO. 24721

WISDOM
Lee Lawrie
Edward H. Ratti, carver
South entry

Wisdom is represented by the figure of a woman, from whose head come rays of light. She holds a book symbolizing the experience of the ages, or the Laws. In the other hand she holds a torch which illuminates the sphere representing the earth. The tower on the left is her temple. The stars, earth and clouds suggest that Wisdom is above earthly derivation.

# Frescoes and Murals

Rotunda

House Wing

Senate Wing

# ROTUNDA

The focal point of the great Rotunda is the canopy of the dome where the fresco, "The Apotheosis of George Washington," may be seen 180 feet above the Rotunda floor. It is 62′2″ in diameter with a concavity of 20′7″ containing 4664 square feet. The figures, which appear life size to the viewer, are approximately 15 feet high. The cartoons or sketches were drawn in 1863 and the fresco, begun in 1864, was completed in about 11 months. It is signed C. Brumidi, 1865.

S. D. Wyeth, a writer of 1866, stated that the "great fresco picture by Brumidi arrests the gaze as though the sky had opened . . ."

It is an allegorical painting which combines mythological and historical figures. In the center, Washington apotheosized, is seated in majesty. On his right is the Goddess of Liberty and on his left is a winged figure, symbolic of Victory and Fame, sounding a trumpet. Surrounding Washington are thirteen maidens, symbolizing the original States, holding a banner emblazoned with the motto "E Pluribus Unum."

The border is composed of six allegorical groupings. Below Washington is *War*, with Freedom holding a shield and accompanied by the Eagle, striking down Tyranny and Kingly Power.

Continuing clockwise, *Art* and *Sciences* are represented by Minerva, Goddess of Wisdom, teaching Benjamin Franklin, Robert Fulton and Samuel F. B. Morse. Young boys listen and learn at her feet.

*Marine*, personified by Neptune bearing his trident, is accompanied by Venus, born of the Sea, holding in her hand the Atlantic Cable.

*Commerce* is represented by Mercury, Protector of Travelers and Merchants. He holds in his hand a bag of gold as he turns toward Robert Morris, financier of the American Revolution. The signature of Brumidi is found on a box at Morris' feet.

*Mechanics*, symbolized by Vulcan, rests his foot on a cannon and surrounding him are man-made products suggesting giant forces of nature can be subservient to human will.

*Agriculture* is represented by Ceres with a cornucopia. America, wearing a red liberty cap, is turning over to Ceres the mastery of a team of horses pulling a reaper. Flora gathers flowers and Pomona bears a basket of fruit.

NEG. NO. 14431

APOTHEOSIS OF WASHINGTON
Constantino Brumidi, fresco, 1865
Canopy of the Dome

303

# ROTUNDA FRIEZE

The frescoed frieze on the interior of the Rotunda is located 58′ above the floor. It is 300′ in circumference and 8′3″ high.

Constantino Brumidi created the designs and completed about one third of the frieze before his death in 1880.

America in History
Landing of Columbus, 1492
Entry of Cortez into the Halls of Montezuma, 1521
Pizarro's Conquest of Peru, 1533
Midnight Burial of De Soto in the Mississippi, 1542
Pocahontas Saving the Life of Capt. John Smith, 1607
Landing of the Pilgrims at Plymouth, Mass., 1620
Penn's Treaty with the Indians, 1682 (approximately half)

The work was continued by Filippo Costaggini. From 1880 to 1888 he used all the designs which Brumidi had prepared to complete the frieze. However, a 31′2″ gap in the design resulted and the frieze was left incomplete. Costaggini's work includes:

Colonization of New England
Peace Between Governor Oglethorpe and the Indians, 1732
Battle of Lexington, 1775
Reading of the Declaration of Independence, 1776
Surrender of Cornwallis at Yorktown, 1781
Death of Tecumseh at the Battle of Thames, 1813
Entry of General Scott into the City of Mexico, 1847
Discovery of Gold in California, 1848

Numerous legislative efforts to appropriate sufficient money and to find a suitable artist to complete the frieze were unsuccessful until 1950 when a resolution providing for completion was signed into law. The Joint Committee on the Library agreed that the unfinished area of the frieze should contain suitable scenes depicting:

The Civil War [1865]
The Spanish-American War [1898]
The Birth of Aviation in the United States [1903]

Allyn Cox was engaged to complete these panels. Mr. Cox finished his painting in the summer of 1953, and that fall he cleaned and restored the original Brumidi-Costaggini work. The frieze was illuminated and dedicated with appropriate ceremonies on May 11, 1954.

## ORIGINAL SKETCHES OF THE ROTUNDA FRIEZE

The original sketch for the Rotunda frieze, from which Constantino Brumidi made the larger cartoons, was presented to the Government by Mrs. Myrtle Cheney Murdock in 1961. It is preserved in the Office of the Architect of the Capitol.

ROTUNDA FRIEZE

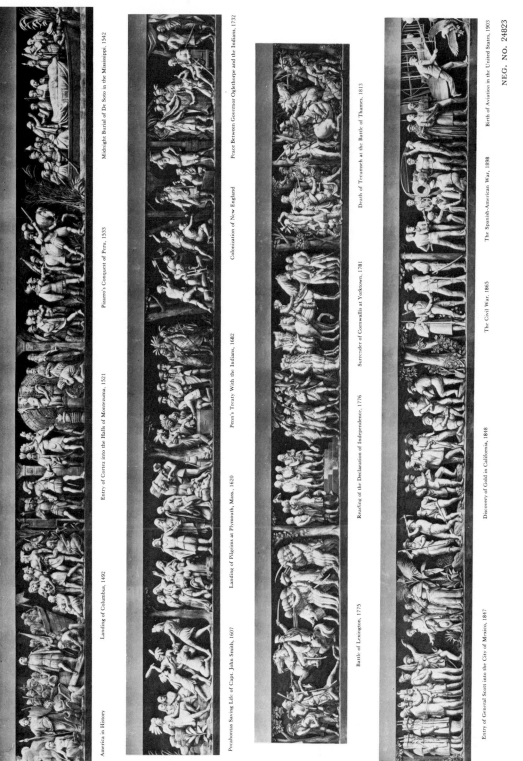

America in History     Landing of Columbus, 1492     Entry of Cortez into the Halls of Montezuma, 1521     Pizarro's Conquest of Peru, 1533     Midnight Burial of De Soto in the Mississippi, 1542

Pocahontas Saving Life of Capt. John Smith, 1607     Landing of Pilgrims at Plymouth, Mass., 1620     Penn's Treaty With the Indians, 1682     Colonization of New England     Peace Between Governor Oglethorpe and the Indians, 1732

Battle of Lexington, 1775     Reading of the Declaration of Independence, 1776     Surrender of Cornwallis at Yorktown, 1781     Death of Tecumseh at the Battle of Thames, 1813

Entry of General Scott into the City of Mexico, 1847     Discovery of Gold in California, 1848     The Civil War, 1865     The Spanish-American War, 1898     Birth of Aviation in the United States, 1903

NEG. NO. 24823

305

NEG. NO. 563

LANDING OF COLUMBUS, 1492

AMERICA IN HISTORY

NEG. NO. 564

PIZARRO'S CONQUEST OF PERU, 1533

ENTRY OF CORTEZ INTO THE HALLS OF MONTEZUMA, 1521

306

NEG. NO. 565

MIDNIGHT BURIAL OF DE SOTO IN THE MISSISSIPPI, 1542

NEG. NO. 566

LANDING OF PILGRIMS AT PLYMOUTH, MASS., 1620

POCAHONTAS SAVING LIFE OF CAPT. JOHN SMITH, 1607

307

NEG. NO. 567

COLONIZATION OF NEW ENGLAND

PENN'S TREATY WITH THE INDIANS, 1682

NEG. NO. 568

BATTLE OF LEXINGTON, 1775

PEACE BETWEEN GOVERNOR OGLETHORPE AND THE INDIANS, 1732

NEG. NO. 569

SURRENDER OF CORNWALLIS AT YORKTOWN, 1781

READING OF THE DECLARATION OF INDEPENDENCE, 1776

NEG. NO. 570

DEATH OF TECUMSEH AT THE BATTLE OF THAMES, 1813

NEG. NO. 571

ENTRY OF GENERAL SCOTT INTO THE CITY OF MEXICO, 1847

NEG. NO. 572

DISCOVERY OF GOLD IN CALIFORNIA, 1848

310

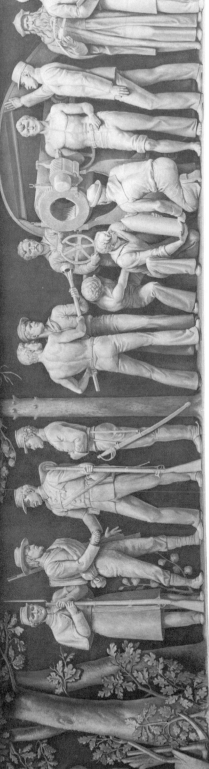

NEG. NO. 573

THE CIVIL WAR, 1865

THE SPANISH-AMERICAN WAR, 1898

NEG. NO. 574

BIRTH OF AVIATION IN THE UNITED STATES, 1903

# HOUSE WING

MEMBERS' PRIVATE DINING ROOM, H–117

CORNWALLIS SUES FOR CESSATION OF HOSTILITIES UNDER THE FLAG OF TRUCE was painted by Constantino Brumidi in 1857. Painted originally on the south wall of the House Chamber, this fresco was covered when the chamber was remodeled in 1950. Its historic beauty was again made visible when it was moved in 1961 to its present location and restored by Allyn Cox. The strap of the briefcase lower right, is signed "C. Brumidi Artist, Citizen of the U.S."

The scene is the headquarters of General Washington at Yorktown on October 17, 1781. Washington is standing, in the act of receiving the letter from the emissary sent by Lord Cornwallis under the flag of truce. The British general requested a 24 hour cessation of hostilities while the terms of surrender might be considered, but Washington, fearing the arrival of the British fleet, gave only a 2 hour cease-fire order. Cornwallis was thus forced into the final surrender which occurred on October 19, 1781. Lord Cornwallis was not present at either of these historic events.

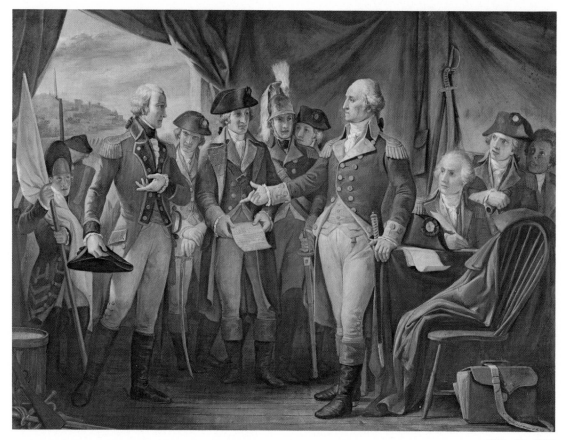

NEG. NO. 22180

CORNWALLIS SUES FOR CESSATION OF HOSTILITIES UNDER THE FLAG OF TRUCE
Constantino Brumidi, 1857, 7' 11½" x 10' 10"
Members' Private Dining Room, H–117

The four lunettes in this room were designed for the Committee on Insular Affairs which met here when Henry Lyman Sayen was commissioned in 1903 to provide suitable paintings. The four scenes are oil on canvas and were in place by 1905.

## RULE OF JUSTICE, north wall

In distinct contrast to the lunette opposite, the center figure represents justice. Commerce, industry and agriculture are depicted symbolically as flourishing. No illustration.

## RULE OF TYRANNY, south wall

The central figure symbolizes tyranny. Represented as powerless under her stifling control are figures representing industry, labor, agriculture, trade and commerce. A veiled figure in the distance symbolizes change. No illustration.

NEG. NO. 26683

## GOOD GOVERNMENT, west wall

The peaceful conditions of the insular possessions under the administration of the United States are portrayed. The central figure is that of a woman carrying a vessel on her shoulder while women on either side pursue domestic activities.

NEG. NO. 26682

## PRIMITIVE AGRICULTURE, east wall

Prior to its installation in 1905, this mural was exhibited in the Pennsylvania Academy of Fine Arts during the Centenary Exhibit. The primitive method of agriculture is depicted.

313

The decorations in this room are by Constantino Brumidi and were the first fresco decorations in the United States Capitol. They were painted in 1855–56 when this room was occupied by the Agriculture Committee. The two murals and the portrayals of the four seasons are in fresco. The wall scenes and medallion heads are in oil.

NEG. NO. 26671

CALLING OF CINCINNATUS FROM THE PLOW, east wall

Early Roman hero of the 4th century B.C. is portrayed as he left his own small farm to save Rome.

NEG. NO. 26670

CALLING OF PUTNAM FROM THE PLOW TO THE REVOLUTION, west wall

Israel Putnam of Massachusetts, one of the heroes of the American Revolution, left his plow in the furrow and hastened to Cambridge and the battle of Breed's Hill, June 16, 1775.

NEG. NO. 26668

HARVESTING GRAIN WITH A McCORMICK REAPER
H–144, north wall.

NEG. NO. 26669

CUTTING GRAIN WITH A SICKLE
H–144, south wall.

AUTUMN    NEG. NO. 26666

WINTER    NEG. NO. 26667

FOUR SEASONS
Constantino Brumidi
H–144

316

SPRING       NEG. NO. 26664

SUMMER       NEG. NO. 26665

317

## House Corridors

The decorations on the ceilings and walls of the east corridor, first floor, in the House wing were executed by Allyn Cox to complement the Brumidi frescoes on the Senate side of the Capitol. Research and preliminary drawings began in 1971, the actual painting started in February 1973, and the work was completed July 22, 1974. Mr. Cox was assisted by Cliff Young and John Roach.

The work, a gift of the U.S. Capitol Historical Society, was authorized by H. J. Res. 169, 92nd Congress.

### Meeting Places of Congress

Albany, N.Y., Old Stadt Huys, 1754   NEG. NO. 38845
New York City, N.Y., Old City Hall, 1765   NEG. NO. 38846
Philadelphia, Pa., Carpenters' Hall, 1774   NEG. NO. 38847
Philadelphia, Pa., Independence Hall, 1775   NEG. NO. 38848
Baltimore, Md., Old Congress Hall, 1776   NEG. NO. 38849
York, Pa., Old Court House, 1777   NEG. NO. 38850
Princeton, N.J., Nassau Hall, 1783   NEG. NO. 38851
Annapolis, Md., State House, 1783   NEG. NO. 38852
Trenton, N.J., French Arms Tavern, 1784   NEG. NO. 38853
New York City, N.Y., Federal Hall, 1785   NEG. NO. 38854
Philadelphia, Pa., Congress Hall, 1790   NEG. NO. 38855
Washington, D.C., U.S. Capitol, 1800   NEG. NO. 38856
Washington, D.C., Blodgett's Hotel, 1814   NEG. NO. 38857
Washington, D.C., Brick Capitol, 1815   NEG. NO. 38858
Washington, D.C., U.S. Capitol, 1829   NEG. NO. 38859
Washington, D.C., U.S. Capitol, 1867   NEG. NO. 38860

### Scenes of Historic Events

Washington and L'Enfant exploring the site of the Capitol, 1791   NEG. NO. 38839
Jefferson presents the competition for the design of a Capitol to the District Commissioners (Johnson, Stuart and Carroll), 1792   NEG. NO. 38861
Washington laying the cornerstone of the Capitol, 1793   NEG. NO. 38838
Burning of the Capitol by the British, 1814   NEG. NO. 38843
First Inauguration (Jackson's) on the steps of the Capitol, 1829   NEG. NO. 38837
Old House Chamber, 1838   NEG. NO. 38841
Rotunda as a hospital, Civil War, 1862   NEG. NO. 38842
Lincoln ordering the building of the dome to continue during the war, 1863   NEG. NO. 38840
Outer lobby of the House during the passage of the Civil Rights Bill, 1866   NEG. NO. 38844

### Portraits of Architects of the Capitol

William Thornton   NEG. NO. 38861
Benjamin H. Latrobe   ALL ON NEG. NO. 39547
Charles Bulfinch
Thomas U. Walter
Edward Clark
Elliott Woods   ALL ON NEG. NO. 39548
David Lynn
J. George Stewart
George M. White

### Portraits of Artists and Planners

Constantino Brumidi   NEG. NO. 38862
John Trumbull   ALL ON NEG. NO. 39549
Pierre Charles L'Enfant
Thomas Crawford
Frederick Law Olmsted

### Sculpture Depicted in the Lunettes

Justice   NEG. NO. 38868
Tripoli Monument   NEG. NO. 38869
George Washington   NEG. NO. 38870
Woodsman   NEG. NO. 38867

### Inscriptions

You Are The Rulers And The Ruled—Adlai Stevenson
One Country One Constitution One Destiny—Daniel Webster
Liberty And Union One And Inseparable—Daniel Webster
Here Sir The People Govern—Alexander Hamilton
This Government/The Offspring Of Our Own Choice/Uninfluenced And Unawed/Has A Just Claim To Your Confidence And Support—George Washington
Man Is Not Made For The State/But The State For Man/And It Derives Its Just Powers/Only From The Consent Of The Governed—Thomas Jefferson
We Have Built No Temple/But The Capitol/We Consult No Common Oracle/But The Constitution—Rufus Choate

NEG. NO. 39540

BURNING OF THE CAPITOL BY THE BRITISH, 1814
ROTUNDA AS A HOSPITAL DURING THE CIVIL WAR, 1862
Allyn Cox, 1974
Corridor, House wing, first floor

319

NEG. NO. 39544

MEETING PLACES OF CONGRESS
Blodgett's Hotel, 1814, Old Brick Capitol, 1815, U.S. Capitol, 1829, and U.S. Capitol, 1867
Allyn Cox, 1974
Corridor, House wing, first floor

320

# SENATE WING

DEMOCRATIC POLICY COMMITTEE ROOM, S–118

Originally, this room was occupied by the Senate Foreign Relations Committee. About 1874 Constantino Brumidi painted the profiles of the early chairmen of that committee on the walls. Later, an unidentified artist added four eagles in distemper to the ceiling decorations.

NEG. NO. 26992

EAGLE
S–118

NEG. NO. 26999

WILLIAM S. ALLEN, 1845–1846
S–118, south wall

NEG. NO. 26997

HENRY CLAY, 1834–1836
S–118, north wall

NEG. NO. 26998

SIMON E. CAMERON, 1871–1877
S–118, east wall

NEG. NO. 26996

CHARLES W. SUMNER, 1861–1871
S–118, west wall

SENATE APPROPRIATIONS COMMITTEE ROOMS, S–127, S–128 AND S–129

The decorations in the Senate Appropriations Committee rooms, S–127, S–128 and S–129, were designed between 1858 and 1871 for the committees which originally used the rooms. The allegorical groupings in S–127 were designed for the Committee on Naval Affairs, those in S–128 and S–129 for the Military Affairs Committee.

S–127     No Illustrations

DECORATIONS BY CONSTANTINO BRUMIDI

> Ancient Porticoes and Antique Vessels
> Indian Heads
> Maidens of the Navy
> Marine Gods and Goddesses

S–128

DECORATIONS BY CONSTANTINO BRUMIDI

> Boston Massacre, 1770
> Battle of Lexington, 1775
> Death of General Wooster, 1777
> Washington at Valley Forge, 1778
> Storming of Stony Point, 1779

Panel and pilaster designs were by Brumidi, and painted by James Leslie. A medallion head of Liberty, surrounded by flags and weapons of war is on the west wall. The ceiling is frescoed with victors' wreaths, shields and other emblems.

S–129     No Illustrations

DECORATIONS BY CARL RAKEMAN, 1909

Generals of the American Revolution

> Horatio Gates (north wall)
> Joseph Warren (south wall)
> George Washington (east wall)
> Anthony Wayne (west wall)

NEG. NO. 26220

WALL PANEL

Representing ancient and modern arms and
 armor of different nations
Designed by Constantino Brumidi; painted
 by James Leslie, 89″ x 20″
S–128

NEG. NO. 26194

BATTLE OF LEXINGTON, 1775
Constantino Brumidi
S–128, south wall

NEG. NO. 26192

BOSTON MASSACRE, 1770
Constantino Brumidi, 1871
S–128, north wall

NEG. NO. 26191

DEATH OF GENERAL WOOSTER, 1777
Constantino Brumidi
S–128, north wall

NEG. NO. 26195

STORMING OF STONY POINT, 1779
Constantino Brumidi, 1871
S–128, east wall

NEG. NO. 26193

WASHINGTON AT VALLEY FORGE, 1778
Constantino Brumidi, 1871
S–128, south wall

LYNDON B. JOHNSON ROOM, S–211

Constantino Brumidi originally decorated this room for the Senate Library, 1858–1867. There are no illustrations. The ceiling murals represent:

> Geography
> History
> Physics
> Telegraph
> Three Graces (4 groups)

OFFICE OF THE VICE PRESIDENT, S–212

In 1876 when S–212 was used by the Sergeant at Arms, Constantino Brumidi painted allegorical designs on the ceiling. There are no illustrations.

> Columbia Welcoming the South back into the Union, signed Brumidi 1876
> Implements of War Destroyed
> Rods United—"E Pluribus Unum"
> Secession and Products of North and South
> War and Strife

SENATE RECEPTION ROOM, S–213

Allegorical groups in the ceiling were painted by Constantino Brumidi 1871–2. They are not illustrated.

CIRCULAR ARCH, south

> La Jurisprudence (Jurisprudence), southeast
> La Force (Strength or Power), northwest
> La Sapience (Wisdom), northeast
> La Prudence (Discretion), southwest

GROINED ARCH, north

> La Guerre (War), west
> La Paix (Peace), east
> Les Sciences (Sciences), north
> Les Arts de l'Industrie (Industrial Arts), south

A painting depicting George Washington in Consultation with Thomas Jefferson and Alexander Hamilton is on the south wall. Portraits of five Senators were added in 1959. See page 34.

NEG. NO. 35116

GEORGE WASHINGTON IN CONSULTATION WITH THOMAS JEFFERSON AND ALEXANDER HAMILTON
Constantino Brumidi, 1870–73
S–213

Constantino Brumidi began his oil and fresco work in this room about 1859. For many years the Presidents used this room as the ceremonial chamber for signing documents. The portraits of the five members of George Washington's first cabinet and symbolic paintings completely cover the walls and ceilings.

There are no illustrations for the symbolic Madonna figures in the ceiling representing Religion, Legislation, Liberty and Executive Authority.

NEG. NO. 35103

GEORGE WASHINGTON
Constantino Brumidi
S–216

NEG. NO. 25905

Thomas Jefferson, Secretary of State
Constantino Brumidi
S–216

328

NEG. NO. 25904

ALEXANDER HAMILTON, Secretary of the Treasury
Constantino Brumidi
S-216

329

NEG. NO. 25906

HENRY KNOX, Secretary of War
Constantino Brumidi
S–216

NEG. NO. 25908

EDMUND RANDOLPH, Attorney General
Constantino Brumidi
S–216

NEG. NO. 25907

Samuel Osgood, Postmaster General
Constantino Brumidi
S–216

NEG. NO. 25901

WILLIAM BREWSTER—Religion
S–216, ceiling

NEG. NO. 25902

CHRISTOPHER COLUMBUS—Discovery
S–216, ceiling

NEG. NO. 25903

BENJAMIN FRANKLIN—History
S–216, ceiling

NEG. NO. 25909

AMERICUS VESPUCIUS—Exploration
S–216, ceiling

## Senate Corridors

The first floor corridors of the Senate wing are lined with mural monochrome medallion portraits and decorative subjects by Constantino Brumidi. They are not illustrated. Negative numbers for black and white prints are included for those works that have been photographed. Each portrait medallion measures approximately 18″ in diameter exclusive of the decorative border.

### Main Corridor

| | |
|---|---|
| Adams (unidentified) | |
| Henry Clay | NEG. NO. 24261 |
| Andrew Jackson | NEG. NO. 23678 |
| Daniel Webster | |
| Chancellor Kent | |
| Justice Joseph Story | |
| Robert R. Livingston, 1878 | |
| 14 oval landscapes in oil | |
| (walls and ceiling), artists are not known | |

### North Corridor

| | |
|---|---|
| Silas Deane | NEG. NO. 23672 |
| Benjamin Franklin | NEG. NO. 23677 |
| Horatio Gates | NEG. NO. 23673 |
| Thomas Jefferson | NEG. NO. 23680 |
| Thomas Mifflin | NEG. NO. 23682 |
| Richard Montgomery | NEG. NO. 23683 |

| | |
|---|---|
| Daniel Morgan | NEG. NO. 23684 |
| Israel Putnam | NEG. NO. 23674 |
| Jonathan Trumbull | NEG. NO. 23688 |
| Joseph Warren | NEG. NO. 23689 |

Cession of Louisiana, lunette

Signing of First Treaty of Peace with Great Britain, 1782, lunette, 1874, after a sketch by Benjamin West

### South Corridor
8 studies in oil (animals)
8 ovals in oil (U.S. Shields)

### West Corridor

| | |
|---|---|
| Charles Carroll | NEG. NO. 23671 |
| John Hancock | NEG. NO. 23675 |
| Francis Hopkinson | NEG. NO. 23676 |
| John Jay | NEG. NO. 23679 |
| Robert R. Livingston | NEG. NO. 23681 |
| Robert Morris | NEG. NO. 23685 |
| Roger Sherman | NEG. NO. 23686 |
| Charles Thomson | NEG. NO. 23687 |

Authority Consults the Written Law, mural
Columbus and the Indian Maiden, mural
Bartolome de Las Casas, the Apostle of the Indians, lunette
Bellona, the Roman Goddess of War, lunette, 1875

NEG. NO. 35105

CESSION OF LOUISIANA
(Negotiations for the acquisition of Louisiana)
Constantino Brumidi, 1875
Senate wing, first floor, north corridor

NEG. NO. 26685

AUTHORITY CONSULTS THE WRITTEN LAW
Constantino Brumidi
Senate wing, first floor, west corridor

NEG. NO. 26686

COLUMBUS AND THE INDIAN MAIDEN
Constantino Brumidi
Senate wing, first floor, west corridor

PATENT CORRIDOR

Constantino Brumidi determined the theme of his decorations here in 1873 from the committees occupying the rooms off this first floor corridor. The Committee on Patents occupied the larger room and the lunettes and ceiling decorations depicting important inventions attest to this influence.

A lunette of Benjamin Franklin in his laboratory is above the door of the room originally used by the Committee on Post Offices and Post Roads.

John Fitch, working on his model of a steamboat, is not illustrated.

The Robert Fulton lunette is the largest and Brumidi has included his steamboat, the *Clermont*, and the New Jersey Palisades in the background. His benefactor, De Witt Clinton, is shown in a portrait on a nearby easel.

NEG. NO. 36384

ROBERT FULTON
Constantino Brumidi
Patent corridor

NEG. NO. 36383

Benjamin Franklin
Constantino Brumidi
Patent corridor

# Exterior Sculpture

Bronze Doors
Fountain
Statues
Tympanums

# ROTUNDA BRONZE DOORS

The bronze doors at the eastern entrance to the Rotunda depicting events in the life of Christopher Columbus were designed and modeled by Randolph Rogers in Rome, Italy in 1858. They were cast in 1861 in Munich, Germany by Ferdinand von Miller at the Royal Bavarian Foundry.

In November 1863 the doors were installed between Statuary Hall and the House extension. Because of their massiveness and great beauty, it was felt they were worthy of a focal location, and in 1871 they were moved to the Rotunda entrance. In 1961 the doors were moved 32 feet east when the East Front of the Capitol was extended.

The doors, also called the Rogers Doors, have two valves with four panels in each valve, surmounted by a semicircular tympanum.

## TYMPANUM

*The Landing of Columbus in the New World* at Guanahani, Watling Island, called San Salvador by Columbus, October 12, 1492.

## LEFT VALVE

*Departure of Columbus From Palos.* Columbus is confiding his son to the monks before he embarks upon his first voyage, August 3, 1492. His ships lie waiting in the harbor.

*Audience at the Court of Ferdinand and Isabella.* Queen Isabella is seated in state, leaning forward and seemingly deeply interested in what Columbus is saying. King Ferdinand is by her side. On April 17, 1492 the agreement between Columbus and their Majesties was signed.

*Columbus' Departure From the Convent of La Rabida,* near Palos, to visit the Spanish Court, 1492. It was to this convent he had come with his small son Diego, weary, penniless and discouraged. He was befriended by Juan Perez, prior of the convent and Confessor to Queen Isabella, and by Lady Bobadilla, an attendant of Isabella, who urged the Queen to assist Columbus in his expedition.

*Columbus Before the Council of Salamanca* is unfolding his grand theory—a new route to the East. In 1487, after long delays, the Council declared the project vain and impossible.

## RIGHT VALVE

*Columbus' First Encounter With the Indians.* One of the sailors is seen carrying an Indian girl prisoner on his shoulders. This action aroused the stern indignation of Columbus.

*Entry of Columbus Into Barcelona.* Waving banners welcome Columbus to the Spanish Court as he returns from his first voyage in 1493.

*Columbus in Chains.* Don Francisco de Bobadilla, sent out by the Court to investigate charges preferred against Columbus, had him placed in chains and returned to Spain, November 1500. On board the vessel, the officers wished to relieve him of his chains, but Columbus replied with deep feeling, "I will wear them as a memento of the gratitude of princes."

Columbus was cleared of the charges, and in 1502 set sail once more for the New World.

*Death of Columbus.* The last rites of the Catholic Church have been administered. Friends and attendants are around him and a priest holds up a crucifix for him to kiss. Columbus returned from his last voyage poor, sick and disconsolate. He sought redress at the Spanish Court, and although he had been cleared of all the charges against him, he failed in his attempt. With the death of Queen Isabella in 1504, Columbus had lost his influence at the Court.

Columbus died at Valladolid, the 20th of May, 1506.

In niches on the sides of the doors and between the panels are sixteen small statues of contemporaries of Columbus. They are identified on the diagram.

*Vespucci*, the much trusted friend of Columbus.

*Ojeda*, an early Spanish adventurer to the New World who lacked fealty to Columbus.

*Cortez*, conqueror of Mexico.

*Perez*, prior of the Convent of La Rabida and firm friend of Columbus.

Standing in pairs on the inside borders are:

*Mendoza*, Archbishop of Toledo and Grand Cardinal of Spain who had great influence at court.

*Alexander VI*, Roman Pontiff.

*Isabella* and *Ferdinand*, Spanish Monarchs.

*Lady Beatrix de Bobadilla*, marchioness of Moya and early friend of Columbus.

*Charles VIII*, King of France.

*Henry VII* of England, a patron of navigation who regarded with favor the theory of Columbus.

*John II*, King of Portugal who reigned during the period of Columbus' first two voyages.

At the top of the last row four additional explorers complete the design.

*Pizarro*, conqueror of Peru.

*Balboa*, Spanish discoverer and adventurer.

*B. Columbus*, brother of Christopher, appointed by him lieutenant governor of the Indies.

*Pinzon*, commander of the *Pinta* who first saw land, September 25, 1492.

### OTHER DECORATIONS

Between the panels and at the top and bottom of the doors are 10 small sculptured heads. They are representative of the historians who have written of Columbus' voyages from his own time to the mid-nineteenth century.

Above the tympanum can be seen the bust of Christopher Columbus, the American Eagle and draped flags. The frame of the door is covered with heraldic emblems. On the extreme edges of the doors are four draped figures representing the continents of Asia, Europe, Africa and America.

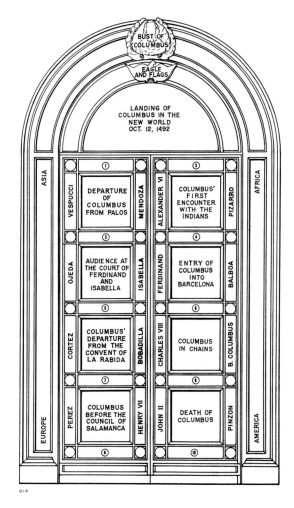

NEG. NO. 19979

ROTUNDA DOORS
Randolph Rogers, bronze, 16'8'' x 9'9''
East Rotunda entrance

345

# HOUSE BRONZE DOORS

The bronze doors at the east portico entrance, House wing, were designed by Thomas Crawford in Rome, Italy in 1855–57. Upon his death William H. Rinehart executed the models from the Crawford sketches, 1863–67.

The models were shipped from Leghorn, Italy in 1867, but remained stored in the Crypt of the Capitol until 1903 when they were cast by Melzar H. Mosman of Chicopee, Massachusetts. The doors were installed in 1905.

The bronze doors of the House wing are comparable to the Senate doors. Each valve consists of three panels and a medallion depicting great events in American history.

## LEFT VALVE

*Wyoming Massacre, Pennsylvania.* During the Revolution a large proportion of the men of Wyoming Valley, Pennsylvania joined the Continental Army. A number of Loyalists remained there, and in 1778 they were joined by the British troops and their Indian allies. The settlers who had taken refuge in Forty Fort, near Wilkes-Barre, were outnumbered 1100 to 400. July 3, 1778 after a desperate battle, the settlers were forced to capitulate. The massacre followed.

*Battle of Lexington.* General Gage, the British Commander in Boston, heard that the Colonists were collecting arms and ammunition. He determined to prevent rebellion by seizing these supplies. The colonists were warned and during the night of April 18, 1775, Paul Revere and William Dawes rode to warn the Minutemen. The British troops were marching toward Concord and met the small Militia. Here on April 19, 1775 occurred the famous "shot heard 'round the World"—the beginning of the Revolutionary War.

*Presentation of Flag and Medal to General Nathanael Greene.* In 1778 Great Britain shifted the attack upon the colonies to the South. Nathanael Greene replaced General Gates as Commander in the South and with the help of loyal American frontiersmen, the British camps were raided. This panel depicts General Greene receiving a medal and flag after the Battle of Eutaw Springs on September 8, 1781 for expelling the British from South Carolina.

*Medallion—Death of General Montgomery.* Late in 1775, Congress sent a two column military expedition to Canada, one under Richard Montgomery via New York, and the other under Benedict Arnold via Maine, hoping to arouse the French Canadians to revolt against the British. The expedition failed. In the attack on Quebec, December 31, 1775, General Montgomery was killed.

## RIGHT VALVE

*Public Reading of the Declaration of Independence at Philadelphia.* On July 4, 1776 the Second Continental Congress adopted the Declaration of Independence. The first public reading was July 8, 1776, when the Declaration of Independence was officially proclaimed in Philadelphia.

*The Signing of the Treaty at Paris Between the United States and Great Britain.* The Revolution ended in October 1781, but it was not until September 3, 1783 that the Treaty of Paris was signed. The panel depicts the negotiations between the United States commissioners and the British representatives. The liberal concessions to the United States were largely due to the efforts of Benjamin Franklin.

*Washington's Farewell to His Officers in New York.* After the Treaty of Peace was signed Washington was leaving New York for Philadelphia. His officers of the war years gathered at Fraunces Tavern, December 4, 1783, to say good-bye. When he entered the room he could scarcely command his voice. He spoke briefly, and they drank a toast. Washington requested each man to come forward and take his hand. General Knox, who stood nearest, was first to clasp his hand. The panel depicts this touching farewell.

*Medallion—Benjamin Franklin in His Studio.* Benjamin Franklin, an inventor, a signer of the Declaration of Independence and the Constitution; a Member of the Continental Congress and Minister to France 1776–1785, is shown in his studio studying electricity.

NEG. NO. 22712

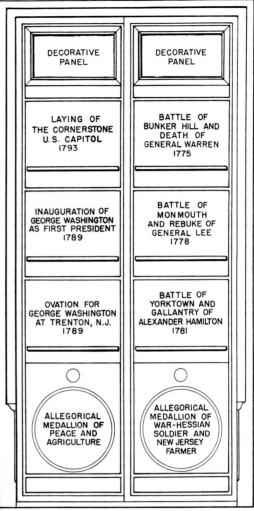

DECORATIVE PANEL — DECORATIVE PANEL

LAYING OF
THE CORNERSTONE
U.S. CAPITOL
1793

BATTLE OF
BUNKER HILL AND
DEATH OF
GENERAL WARREN
1775

INAUGURATION OF
GEORGE WASHINGTON
AS FIRST PRESIDENT
1789

BATTLE OF
MONMOUTH
AND REBUKE OF
GENERAL LEE
1778

OVATION FOR
GEORGE WASHINGTON
AT TRENTON, N.J.
1789

BATTLE OF
YORKTOWN AND
GALLANTRY OF
ALEXANDER HAMILTON
1781

ALLEGORICAL
MEDALLION OF
PEACE AND
AGRICULTURE

ALLEGORICAL
MEDALLION OF
WAR-HESSIAN
SOLDIER AND
NEW JERSEY
FARMER

O. I. P.

SENATE DOORS
Designed by Thomas Crawford, bronze
Executed by William H. Rinehart,
    14′ 5½″ x 7′ 4″
East Senate portico entrance

# AMATEIS BRONZE DOORS

The Amateis bronze doors were designed and cast for the main central entrance of the West Front. They were completed in 1910, but they could not be placed because the enabling legislation for the improvement of the West Front was not enacted. The doors were exhibited at the Corcoran Gallery of Art for four years. In 1914 they were loaned to the Smithsonian Institution where they were on exhibition in the Natural History Building until 1967. At that time they were returned to the Capitol and in 1972 they were placed on display.

The doors consist of eight panels and a transom depicting allegorical and symbolic accomplishments of America.

There are twenty-eight medallions and eighteen statuettes bordering the eight panels and the transom.

## TRANSOM

*Apotheosis of America.* America, in a chariot drawn by Lions, is symbolic of Strength. The Lions are led by a Child, signifying the superiority of the Intellect over Brute Force. At the sides of the chariot are allegorical figures of Education, Architecture, Painting, Literature, Music, Sculpture, Commerce, Mining and Industry. Statuettes of Benjamin Franklin and Thomas Jefferson stand on either side in the border of the panel. Medallions in the four corners are Horace Mann, educator, George Peabody, financier of educational institutions, Johns Hopkins, philanthropist, and Ralph Waldo Emerson, philosopher.

## LEFT VALVE

*Jurisprudence* is represented by the Supreme Court presided over by Chief Justice John Marshall. A bust of George Washington is shown above the chair of the Chief Justice. Statuettes on the left and right are of Daniel Webster and James Madison. Above are medallions of Patrick Henry, patriot, Rufus Choate, lawyer, and Chief Justice Roger B. Taney.

*Sciences.* Scientific workers from Hipparchus, Greek astronomer, to Charles R. Darwin. At the sides are statuettes of Oliver W. Gibbs, chemist, and Joseph Henry, physicist. The medallions portray James D. Dana, geologist, Simon Newcomb, astronomer, Alexander Graham Bell, inventor of the telephone, and Samuel F. B. Morse, inventor of the telegraph.

*Fine Arts.* Figures of Virgil, Dante, Shakespeare, Goethe, Hugo, Palestrina, Beethoven, Rossini and Homer. Above them is a flying figure of Genius. The statuettes at the sides are of Edgar Allen Poe, writer, and William Thornton, first Architect of the U.S. Capitol. The medallions portray Gilbert Stuart, painter, and Henry Kirke Brown, sculptor.

*Mining.* Scene at a mine. On each side of this panel are statuettes of James W. Marshall, discoverer of gold in California, and Alexander L. Holley, mining engineer. The medallions portray E. B. Case, engineer, Clarence King, geologist, and Abram Hewitt, industrialist.

## RIGHT VALVE

*Agriculture.* A typical harvest scene. The statuettes are of Samuel G. Morton, physician and ethnologist, and James Wilson, agriculturist. The medallions portray John Pitkin Norton, agricultural chemist, Senator Justin S. Morrill, and Benjamin Bussey, agricultural chemist.

*Iron and Electricity.* Iron and electric workers. The statuettes are of Peter Cooper, philanthropist, and Henry A. Rowland, physicist. Medallions show Matthias W. Baldwin, founder of the locomotive works and Thomas Alva Edison, inventor.

*Engineering.* Workers laying a railroad track. A bridge is in the background. Statuettes show James B. Eads, builder of the St. Louis bridge, and Thomas L. Casey, engineer. Medallions portray Washington A. Roebling, builder of the Brooklyn bridge, and Stevens, builder of the transcontinental railroads.

*Naval Architecture and Commerce* is represented by a figure typifying Architecture, showing Commerce, Industry and Agriculture the places on a globe where they can dispose of their wares. The globe is held by a Youth. A sailor is holding a flag surmounted by a liberty cap, significant of an open door policy. Statuettes portray Robert Fulton, inventor of the steamboat, and John Ericsson, designer of the *Monitor*. Medallions depict Eli Whitney, inventor of the cotton gin, Elias Howe, inventor of the sewing machine, John C. Fremont, the "Pathfinder," Cyrus W. Field, financier of the Atlantic Cable, and John Lenthall, naval constructor.

NEG. NO. 36090

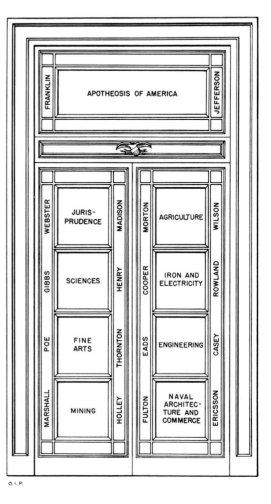

O. I. P.

Amateis Doors
Signed l.l. L. Amateis, Sculptor, Washington,
    D.C., 1910; bronze, 13′ 10″ x 7′ 8½″
Center building, first floor

# BARTHOLDI FOUNTAIN

Designed by the same sculptor who created the Statue of Liberty, this fountain was sent by the French government for the 1876 Centennial Exposition in Philadelphia. It was purchased by the Committee on Public Buildings and Grounds and moved to the Botanic Garden, then on the mall. When the Garden was relocated in 1932, the fountain was also moved to its present location.

Illuminated originally with gas, it is intended to embody an allegorical representation of the elements of *Water* and *Light*.

It is 30′ high, weighs 40 tons, basin 26′ in diameter, statue 11′.

NEG. NO. 34060

BARTHOLDI FOUNTAIN
Frederic Auguste Bartholdi, iron bronzed
Purchased 1877
Botanic Garden

# DISCOVERY AND RESCUE

Originally located on the south cheek block, east central front steps, the grouping became so badly deteriorated that in 1958 when the Extension of the East Front began, "Discovery" was crated and placed in storage. Overall dimensions are 15'11½" high, 8'4½" wide and 6'½" deep.

As a companion piece to "Discovery," "Rescue" was placed on the north cheek block, east central front steps. It, too, was removed and placed in storage when the Extension of the East Front began. Overall dimensions are 11'9" high, 10'2" wide and 7'3" deep.

NEG. NO. 100

NEG. NO. 102

DISCOVERY OF AMERICA
Luigi Persico, marble
Erected 1844
Purchased by Stats. L., vol. 5, p. 173
Transferred to Smithsonian Institution 1976

RESCUE
Horatio Greenough, marble
Erected 1853
Purchased by Congress, March 3, 1837
Transferred to Smithsonian Institution 1976

# STATUE OF FREEDOM

Surmounting the Dome of the Capitol and facing east is the bronze Statue of Freedom. It was designed by Thomas Crawford in Rome, Italy, in 1856. The plaster model was received in 1858 and the casting was done in the shops of another sculptor, Clark Mills, in northeast Washington, D.C.

The figure is that of a woman clad in flowing draperies. Her right hand rests upon the hilt of a sheathed sword, and her left holds a wreath and shield. At her waist a brooch composed of the letters "U.S." holds her robes in place. The head is covered by a helmet encircled with stars and topped with a bold arrangement of feathers and an eagle's head.

Freedom is 19'6" high, weighs 14,985 pounds and cost $23,796.82. Its placement was completed December 2, 1863.

From 1890 to 1967 the plaster model of the Statue of Freedom was on exhibition in the Smithsonian Institution. It is now in storage.

NEG. NO. 27751

STATUE OF FREEDOM
Thomas Crawford, bronze, 19'6"
Dome of the United States Capitol

See also frontispiece

# JUSTICE AND HISTORY

The two draped figures of Justice and History recline against a globe. Justice is supporting a volume bearing the inscription "Justice, Law, Order," and her right hand rests on a pair of scales. History holds a scroll incised "History, July 1776."

Overall length of the sculpture is 11'2'', length of the reclining figure of History 5'4'', length of the reclining figure of Justice 5'10'', height of each figure 3'10'' and the depth of the sculpture is 2'2''.

These figures became irreparably disfigured through deterioration and granulation of the marble. Authorization and appropriation to make replicas from casts of the original Justice and History were provided for by P.L. 93–145, 93rd Congress. Francesco Tonelli of the Vermont Marble Co. was the carver. The reproductions were placed December 1974.

The original figures may be seen in the Capitol terminal of the Senate subway.

NEG. NO. 36281

JUSTICE AND HISTORY
Thomas Crawford, marble
Placed 1863 as part of the Senate wing construction
Above Senate bronze doors, east portico

# STATUES OF WAR AND PEACE

Luigi Persico executed marble statues of War and Peace in Italy. They arrived at the Capitol in 1834 where they were placed in niches on the East Front portico. Through the years, deterioration of serious proportions affected both statues and in 1958 they were removed when the East Front was extended. The defaced figures were mended so that plaster models could be made from the originals by George Giannetti of Washington, D.C. Carvers were then able to reproduce the new figures in Vermont marble and they were placed in 1960. The 1958 plaster models of War and Peace may be seen in the Cannon House Office Building rotunda, subway level. The original marble figure of War was transferred to the Smithsonian Institution in 1976.

NEG. NO. 20505

NEG. NO. 20504

WAR

Carved in 1958 after the original by Luigi Persico

Niche right of east central entrance

Clad in the costume of a Roman warrior, War stands with a firm, sedate countenance and with no evidence of rage or fury. He assumes the attitude of listening to Peace, who stands on his right.

PEACE

Carved 1958 after the original by Luigi Persico

Niche left of east central entrance

Draped in simple flowing robes, Peace holds in her left hand a fruit-bearing olive branch which she extends toward War. Her attitude is one of sympathy for mankind.

356

# MAJESTY OF LAW

# SPIRIT OF JUSTICE

A companion piece to Spirit of Justice, the male figure of the Majesty of Law is portrayed as one who instills reverence for the law and typifies supreme authority and great dignity.

The sheathed sword in his right hand is a symbol of valor. His left hand rests on a book containing the laws of this land with the Seal of the United States on the cover.

The Spirit of Justice is represented by a female figure, likened to Pallas Athene, the great civic goddess who was also wise in the industries of Peace.

In her right hand she holds aloft a lighted lamp symbolizing truth and righteousness. Her left hand around the shoulder of a small boy signifies Temperance with Justice.

NEG. NO. 28642

NEG. NO. 28644

MAJESTY OF LAW
C. Paul Jennewein, 1964, marble, approximately
   10'4" x 6'
Rayburn House Office Building, Independence
   Avenue, west pylon

SPIRIT OF JUSTICE
C. Paul Jennewein, 1964, marble, approximately
   10'4" x 6'
Rayburn House Office Building, Independence
   Avenue, east pylon

# STATUE OF CHIEF JUSTICE JOHN MARSHALL

The sculptor has given us the posture of Marshall as the great jurist, sitting in the chair he used for so many years, rendering a judicial decision.

On the marble base is incised: "John Marshall, Chief Justice of the United States. Erected by the Bar and the Congress of the United States, A.D. MDCCCLXXXIV." On the north side of the base is a panel in relief, "Minerva Dictating the Constitution to Young America." A companion panel on the south side, "Victory Leading Young America to Swear Fidelity at the Altar of the Union," is depicted in the accompanying photograph.

NEG. NO. 35111

John Marshall
William Wetmore Story, bronze, 6'11"
Signed l. base W. W. Story, Roma, 1883
Capitol Grounds, West Front

# RHYTONS

These marble accents occur at each side of the wing motives at the east and west ends of the building. The designer, a member of the architectural firm who designed the building, modeled the rhytons after the ancient Greek drinking horn with a mythical chimera with bended knees.

The Ram's head is representative of Wisdom, Power, Strength of Purpose, Defender of Right. The Horn, or Cornucopia, is the classic symbol of abundance and plenty. The rhytons rest on a calyx of water leaves.

NEG. NO. 33261

Rhytons (8)
Designed by W. H. Livingston, Sr.
Placed 1964, marble, 12½ tons
Rayburn House Office Building

# ROBERT A. TAFT MEMORIAL

The simple strength and quiet dignity of the bell tower memorial is symbolic of the man it represents. The shaft of Tennessee marble houses the 27 extraordinarily matched bells which were cast in the Paccard Bell Foundry in Annecy, France. They strike the hour and chime on the quarter hour. By Congressional resolution they play the Star Spangled Banner at 2 p.m. on the 4th of July. During Christmas week religious carols may be heard, and on Sunday hymns are played at four different times.

The Taft Memorial, authorized by Senate Concurrent Resolution 44, 84th Congress, was constructed with funds received by public subscription. Located on the grounds directly north of the Capitol the tower rises 100′ and is 11′ thick and 32′ wide. It rests on a base 55′ x 45′ and 15′ high. Standing on the base is the 10′ bronze statue of Robert A. Taft, and behind it are incised the words:

This Memorial to Robert A. Taft, presented by the people to the Congress of the United States, stands as tribute to the honesty, indomitable courage and high principles of free government symbolized by his life.

The memorial was dedicated and accepted by the Congress of the United States April, 14, 1959.

NEG. NO. 20747

Robert A. Taft Memorial, 1959
Designed by Douglas W. Orr, architect
United States Capitol Grounds

NEG. NO. 35112

Robert A. Taft, statue
Wheeler Williams, bronze, 1959, 10′
Base of Taft Memorial

# TYMPANUMS

America, the central figure, rests her right arm on a shield inscribed "USA" which is supported by an altar bearing the inscription "July 4, 1776." She points to Justice holding the scales and in whose right hand a scroll is inscribed, "Constitution, 17 September 1787." To America's left is an Eagle and the figure of Hope, who rests her arm on an anchor. This grouping conveys the thought that while we cultivate justice, we may strive for success.

The original sandstone figures were executed by Luigi Persico in 1825–28 after a design suggested by President John Quincy Adams. When the East Front was extended, the badly deteriorated figures were removed and restored so that plaster models could be made. From these models the reproductions were carved in Georgia White marble.

The pediment is 81′ 6″ in length and the figures are 9′ high. The plaster models for the reproductions are located in the rotunda of the Cannon House Office Building, subway level. The original sandstone figures are in storage.

NEG. NO. 20892

GENIUS OF AMERICA
Luigi Persico, sandstone, 1825–28
Bruno Mankowski, marble, 1959–60
East Central Pediment

361

An allegorical group consisting of two figures "Peace Protecting Genius," fills the center of the pediment. An armed Peace, stands erect, draped in a mantle which almost completely hides her breastplate and coat of mail. Her left arm rests on her buckler, which is supported by the altar at her side. In the background is the olive tree of peace. Her right arm is extended in a gesture of protection over the youthful and winged figure of Genius, who nestles confidently at her feet and holds in his right hand the torch of Immortality. The composition is completed by two other groups, symbolizing and typifying the two great fundamental powers of labor, the two great sources of wealth—Agriculture and Industry. A wave at either end of the sculpture symbolizes the Atlantic and Pacific Oceans.

The figures were modeled in Paris, France and Washington, D.C., 1911–1914; carved in Georgia White marble by the Piccirilli Brothers of New York City, 1914–1916 and unveiled August 2, 1916. Extreme length of pediment 80'; height at center about 12'; length of sculpture about 60'.

The plaster models were given to the United States Government in March 1963 by Mrs. Armistead Peter III, a stepdaughter of the artist. They were placed in the Capitol terminal of the subway leading to the Rayburn House Office Building.

362

NEG. NO. 34881

APOTHEOSIS OF DEMOCRACY
Paul Wayland Bartlett, marble, 1916
House Pediment, East Front

The center figure is America with an eagle at her side and the sun at her back. On her left, representing the early days in America, are a woodsman, hunter, Indian chief, Indian mother and child, and an Indian grave. On her right the progress of civilization is depicted in the figures of the soldier, merchant, two youths, the schoolmaster and child, and the mechanic. Completing this side of the tympanum are sheaves of wheat, symbolic of fertility, and an anchor, symbolic of hope, in contrast to the grave at the opposite end of the sculpture of the tympanum.

The figures were modeled in Rome, Italy in 1854; carved at the Capitol 1855–59 from Lee, Massachusetts marble; erected in 1863. The extreme length of the pediment is 80'; height at center about 12'; and the length of the sculpture is about 60'.

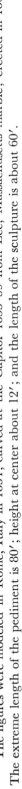

NEG. NO. 34882

PROGRESS OF CIVILIZATION
Thomas Crawford, marble, 1863
Senate Pediment, East Front

# RAYBURN HOUSE OFFICE BUILDING

The symbolic American Eagle spreads his wings in the tympanum above the Independence Avenue entrance. The sculpture was part of the Rayburn House Office Building construction.

NEG. NO. 36577

EAGLE
C. Paul Jennewein, 1964, marble
Rayburn House Office Building

# Miscellaneous Works of Art

Sculpture

Vases

Window and Laylights

# SCULPTURE

NEG. NO. 35107

"CORNCOB" CAPITALS (6), 1809
Designed by Benjamin H. Latrobe; modeled and
 carved by Giuseppe Franzoni, sandstone
East Front entry, first floor vestibule

NEG. NO. 33882

CORINTHIAN CAPITAL, 1825
Crypt

 Original column cap and base of sandstone were
removed from the East Front when it was extended and
duplicated in marble 1958–1961.

NEG. NO. 19914

TOBACCO CAPITALS (16), 1818
Designed by Benjamin H. Latrobe; modeled and
 carved by Francisco Iardella, sandstone
Lobby of the small rotunda, Senate wing,
 second floor

 The tobacco motiff is also used in the capitals of the
28 columns in the Hall of Columns, House wing, first
floor, and were carved about 1855.

NEG. NO. 35108

CAR OF HISTORY (CLOCK)
Carlo Franzoni, marble, 1819
Statuary Hall, north entrance

Clio, the Muse, representing History, stands in the winged car of Time, recording events as they occur. The car rests on a marble globe on which the signs of the zodiac are carved in relief. The chariot wheel is the face of the clock. The works are by Simon Willard.

367

NEG. NO. 18679

EAGLE
Giuseppe Valaperta, sandstone, 1816
Statuary Hall on the frieze of the entablature below the statue of Liberty

NEG. NO. 18677

EAGLE
Artist and date unknown, gilt wood, 72″ wing span
S–228, Old Senate Chamber

As early as 1834 there was reference to a gilt eagle in the Old Senate Chamber above the canopy over the chair of the presiding officer. Although specific information is unknown, an eagle has traditionally been in the Chamber.

INDIAN AND THE PIONEER
William H. Rinehart, 1857, bronze, 3′ high

These figures stood on either side of an elaborately carved wooden clock case which was removed and stored after the remodeling of the House Chamber 1940–1951. No illustration.

INDIAN FOUNTAIN
William H. Rinehart, bronze, 1857
SB-14

Acquired by action of the Joint Committee on the Library, 1876, when extensive remodeling no longer left a place for it in the Post Office. The bowl is about 16″ in diameter; the figure is 13″ high.

369

NEG. NO. 35113

MASK
Unknown artist, bronze, 1857
SB–14

    This mask was over the north entrance to the House Chamber from 1857 to 1950. It was removed when the House Chamber was remodeled in 1950.

NEG. NO. 32199

PERICLES
Artist and date unknown, bronze, 19½″
H–216, House Appropriations Committee
No records

NEG. NO. 32198

PHIDIAS
Artist and date unknown, bronze, 19″
H–216, House Appropriations Committee
No records

NEG. NO. 37056

PIONEERS OF THE WEST

NEG. NO. 37057

SETTLERS OF THE EAST COAST

These groups were made in plaster by Paul Manship in 1965 as suggested statuary for the cheek blocks on the East Central Front when it was extended 1958–1961. They are on display in the Crypt.

NEG. NO. 25223                    NEG. NO. 25224

SEVRES VASES, 66¾″ high, 25″ diameter
Gifts of the Republic of France, 1918
H–207, Rayburn Room

NEG. NO. 25900                    NEG. NO. 25899

SEVRES VASES, 68¾″ high, 28″ diameter
Gifts of the Republic of France, 1918
Senate Lobby

NEG. NO. 26349

BALUSTERS AND RAILS
Designed by Constantino Brumidi, 1857, bronze
Two stairways in the Senate wing and two in the House wing are decorated with magnificent designs
in bronze. Modeled by Edmond Baudin and cast in Philadelphia by Archer, Warner, Miskey and
Co., 1857–59

NEG. NO. 26350

DETAILS OF BRONZE STAIRWAYS

NEG. NO. 37087

NEG. NO. 35114

CIRCULAR WINDOWS (4)
J. and G. H. Gibson Company of Philadelphia, 1859–60, 59″ diameter
First floor landing on each grand stairway

Three windows are emblazoned with the shield, eagle and flags of the United States and the motto, "E Pluribus Unum." The center of the window on the East Senate stairway was accidentally destroyed and was replaced with embossed glass.

NEG. NO. 37086

PRAYER WINDOW
Anonymous gift, 1955, 3'8½'' x 9'3⅜''
H–234

This window is the focal point of the small, private room which is used by Senators and Representatives for meditation. The seal of the United States, a biblical quotation, and the names of the fifty states surround the central figure of George Washington kneeling.

NEG. NO. 22363

GEORGE WASHINGTON MEMORIAL WINDOW
Signed Maria Herndl; 1901, 39″ x 62¾″
Purchased 1910 by Joint Committee on the Library
Senators' private dining room, first floor

General Washington is pictured in conference with General Lafayette and Baron von Steuben in a Revolutionary War scene of 1780. This work of art was loaned to the Smithsonian Institution in 1932 where it was on display until 1962 when it was returned to the Capitol and installed in the dining room.

378

NEG. NO. 35110

RECTANGULAR LAYLIGHTS (4)
J. and G. H. Gibson Company of Philadelphia, 1859–60
Grand stairways: House wing 2; Senate wing 2

379

# Appendix I

# MANTELS

Reconstruction of the original North and South wings of the Capitol, burned by the British in 1814, was progressing rapidly when Charles Bulfinch became the third Architect of the Capitol in 1818. The work was being accomplished according to the designs of Bulfinch's predecessor, Benjamin Henry Latrobe, and had progressed to the point where Bulfinch had no viable alternative except to continue with that plan. Among the items that he inherited were fifty marble mantels that he installed between 1819 and 1829.

In spite of alterations, additions, fires and other vagaries of time that have occurred since the Latrobe and Bulfinch period, a number of the finest examples of mantel design of the Federal Period still exist as originally installed in the Capitol.

Notable among these are two finely carved marble mantels located in the Old Senate Chamber. These two resulted from an original order for four mantels, executed from drawings prepared by Giovanni Andrei at the direction of Latrobe. They were ordered from James Traquair in Philadelphia about 1812, but because of wartime shipping dangers, they were not sent to Washington, and thus were saved by their absence from the British incendiary fire of 1814. When the Capitol was rebuilt, these mantels, crated and waiting for three years, were installed and Traquair was paid $800 for them in 1817. The other two mantels that were part of the original order have never been located.

During the rebuilding of 1815–1819, six mantels were obtained from James Hodge of Albany, New York, and at least four others were purchased from the Milford Marble Co. of New Haven, Connecticut. The identities and locations of these mantels are not known.

By the time Thomas U. Walter became Architect of the Capitol in 1851 and designed the present dome and House and Senate wings, styles had changed. The slender reeding and vertical lines popular 50 years earlier had given way to the curving opulence of the Victorian Era, and these new styles were incorporated into the mantels of the new wings. At the same time, some occupants of the older central part of the building, who wished to be more in keeping with the times, had their earlier mantels removed and replaced with the new styles which had semicircular openings and, in some cases, grates for the burning of coal.

Several mantels of this later design may be found on the various floors of the West Central wing. That area was formerly occupied by the Library of Congress and rebuilt after a fire destroyed the Library in 1851. The Library moved to its new building in 1897, and in 1900 the space was reconstructed for offices.

In carrying out the work of extending the East Central Front, the mantels of the Old Senate Chamber were used as the inspiration for the designs of the new mantels in the Senate Conference Room and House Reception Room.

Selected photographs show examples of the many mantels now in the Capitol.

NEG. NO. 25711

ROOM HB–25
Thomas U. Walter, 1857

NEG. NO. 24202

ROOM H–110
Bulfinch period

NEG. NO. 24204

ROOM H–116
Bulfinch period

NEG. NO. 34363

ROOM H–150
Bulfinch period

383

NEG. NO. 24205

ROOM H–151
Bulfinch period

NEG. NO. 24893

ROOM H–162
Bulfinch period

NEG. NO. 25082

ROOM H–157
Bulfinch period

NEG. NO. 25294

ROOM H–163
Bulfinch period

384

NEG. NO. 25295

ROOM H–164
Bulfinch period

NEG. NO. 23943

RAYBURN ROOM, H–207
East Front Extension, 1960

NEG. NO. 27620

ROOM H–209
Thomas U. Walter, 1857

NEG. NO. 24892

ROOM S–150
Bulfinch period

NEG. NO. 24434

SENATE CONFERENCE ROOM, S–207
East Front Extension, 1960

NEG. NO. 35498

SENATE MARBLE ROOM, S–215
Thomas U. Walter

NEG. NO. 16904

OLD SENATE CHAMBER, S–228
Latrobe, 1812

NEG. NO. 16906

OLD SENATE CHAMBER, S–228
Latrobe, 1812

386

# MODELS OF UNITED STATES CAPITOL

NEG. NO. 26357

EAST FRONT EXTENSION
Emile Garet, 1903–04
Length: 12′ 7″; width: 5′9½″
Height: 4′9½″ (from platform to top of statue)
Base: 13′½″ x 6′ x 4″
Scale: 100′ = ⅛″

This study model in plaster was constructed by the Office of the Architect of the Capitol through the employment of Emile Garet, architectural sculptor, as part of a 1904 report for the extension and completion of the U.S. Capitol. Fifty-eight years later the East Front extension became a reality.

The model was constructed so that the extension could be removed to compare the Capitol as it then existed with the proposed changes of 1904. The delicate carvings and attention to detail caused it to be considered a work of art. It was sent to many expositions, among them the Panama Pacific International Exposition in San Francisco, California, 1915; the Sesquicentennial Exposition, Philadelphia, Pennsylvania, 1926; International Exposition, Seville, Spain, 1928–29, where it received a gold medal as the outstanding feature of the exhibit of the Commission of Fine Arts; and the Great Lakes Exposition, Cleveland, Ohio in 1937.

The much traveled model was placed on display in the Crypt of the Capitol from 1938 to 1976, when it was moved to the subway rotunda of the Cannon House Office Building.

NEG. NO. 30859

WEST FRONT EXTENSION
Hadley Associates, Inc., 1966
Length: 47″; width: 22″
Height: 18″
Base: 4′ 8″ x 7′
Scale: $\frac{1}{16}$″ = 1′

This model is based on the plan for the Extension of the West Central Front recommended by Associate Architects and approved by the Commission for the Extension of the United States Capitol June 17, 1966. It is made of white metal or aluminum and acrylic plastic, with various materials used in the site surrounding the model. The walnut base and glass showcase were also made by the modeler.

The model is on display in the Crypt of the Capitol.

# MOTTOES

These mottoes are incised in marble and are not illustrated.

*In God We Trust.* House Chamber, placed 1962 by House Res. 740, 87th Congress. Three stars behind the Speaker's rostrum were removed to place the inscription. The same motto is found in the Longworth House Office Building and the Dirksen Senate Office Building.

The following mottoes were added to the Senate Chamber when it was remodeled in 1950.

*Annuit Coeptis.* God has favored our undertakings. Over east doorway.

*Novus Ordo Seclorum.* A new order of the ages is born. Over west doorway.

*In God We Trust.* Over South entrance.

*E Pluribus Unum.* One out of many. Panel behind Vice President's chair.

# PLAQUES AND MARKERS

A circular 3⅞ inch bronze marker on the floor of Statuary Hall (the Old Hall of the House) marks the place John Quincy Adams, then a Member of the House, had his desk. Here on February 21, 1848, he fell to the floor mortally ill and died two days later in a nearby room. The marker was placed in 1888. Not illustrated.

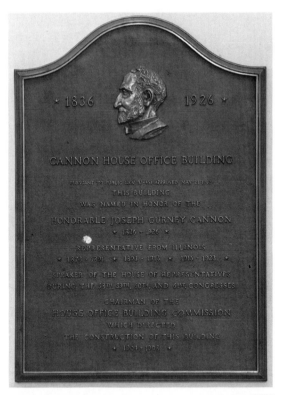

NEG. NO. 33886

JOSEPH G. CANNON, Speaker
Sculptor: Frank Eliscu, bronze, 28″ x 40″
Placed January 31, 1969
Cannon House Office Building rotunda

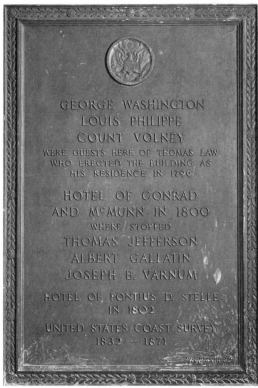

NEG. NO. 27251

CONRAD AND McMUNN HOTEL
In storage, bronze

This plaque was removed in 1929 from the hotel which occupied the site of the Longworth House Office Building.

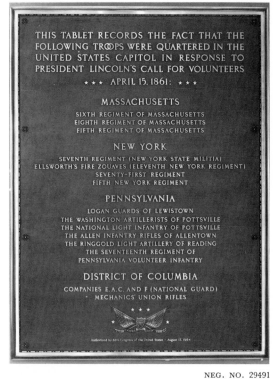

NEG. NO. 29491

CIVIL WAR TROOPS
Placed December 17, 1965
by House Res. 530, 88th Congress,
bronze, 41¾″ x 55¾″
East Front entrance, first floor, House side

NEG. NO. 35106

COMMEMORATING THE LAYING OF THE U.S. CAPITOL CORNERSTONE, 1793
Placed during George Washington Bicentennial, 1932, stone, 4′ x 2′ x 1′4″
Old Supreme Court entrance, first floor, East Front

Beneath this tablet the corner stone of the
Capitol of the United States of America
was laid by
George Washington
First President September 18, 1793.

\* \* \* \* \*      \* \* \* \* \*      \* \* \* \* \*

On the Hundredth Anniversary
in the year 1893
In presence of the Congress the Executive and the Judiciary
a vast concourse of the grateful people
of the District of Columbia commemorated the event.

\* \* \* \* \* \* \* \* \* \* \* \* \* \* \* \*

| | |
|---|---|
| Grover Cleveland | President of the United States. |
| Adlai Ewing Stevenson | Vice President. |
| Charles Frederick Crisp | Speaker, House of Representatives. |
| Daniel Wolsey Voorhees | Chairman Joint Committee of Congress. |
| Lawrence Gardner | Chairman Citizens Committee. |

NEG. NO. 24611

CENTENNIAL OF THE U.S. CAPITOL CORNERSTONE
Placed 1893, bronze, 53¾″ x 80″
Old Supreme Court entrance, first floor,
East Front

NEG. NO. 951

DECLARATION OF INDEPENDENCE
Gift of Michael Francis Doyle, 1932, bronze,
Rotunda

NEG. NO. 11620

HOUSE OF REPRESENTATIVES FIRST MEETING PLACE IN THE CAPITOL
Placed 1952, bronze, 24"x 28"
Outside Senate Disbursing Office, S–233

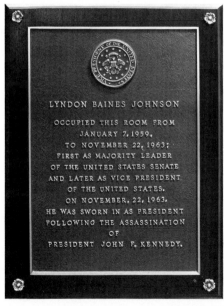

LYNDON B. JOHNSON
Bronze, 10″ x 14″
Placed June 25, 1964
S-211

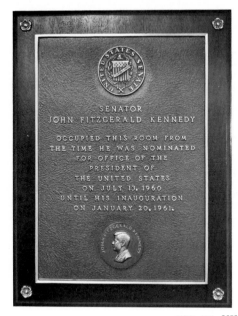

NEG. NO. 26728

JOHN F. KENNEDY
Bronze, 10″ x 14″
Placed June 30, 1964
S-210

NEG. NO. 20486

IN GOD WE TRUST
Placed 1961, two identical bronzes
(1) Longworth House Office Building, main lobby, east wall
(2) Dirksen Office Building, southwest entrance, west wall

NEG. NO. 40510

THE JOHN W. MCCORMACK ANNUAL AWARD OF EXCELLENCE
Designed by the Office of the Architect of the Capitol, bronze on mahogany, 31″ x 42″, placed December 17, 1970
Corridor opposite H-209, Speaker's Office

394

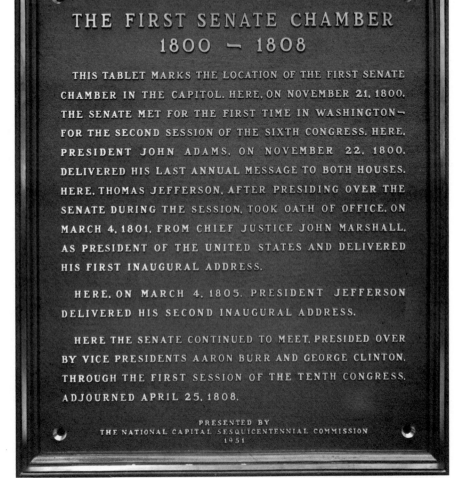

THE FIRST SENATE CHAMBER
1800 — 1808

THIS TABLET MARKS THE LOCATION OF THE FIRST SENATE
CHAMBER IN THE CAPITOL. HERE, ON NOVEMBER 21, 1800,
THE SENATE MET FOR THE FIRST TIME IN WASHINGTON—
FOR THE SECOND SESSION OF THE SIXTH CONGRESS. HERE,
PRESIDENT JOHN ADAMS, ON NOVEMBER 22, 1800,
DELIVERED HIS LAST ANNUAL MESSAGE TO BOTH HOUSES.
HERE, THOMAS JEFFERSON, AFTER PRESIDING OVER THE
SENATE DURING THE SESSION, TOOK OATH OF OFFICE, ON
MARCH 4, 1801, FROM CHIEF JUSTICE JOHN MARSHALL,
AS PRESIDENT OF THE UNITED STATES AND DELIVERED
HIS FIRST INAUGURAL ADDRESS.

HERE, ON MARCH 4, 1805, PRESIDENT JEFFERSON
DELIVERED HIS SECOND INAUGURAL ADDRESS.

HERE THE SENATE CONTINUED TO MEET, PRESIDED OVER
BY VICE PRESIDENTS AARON BURR AND GEORGE CLINTON,
THROUGH THE FIRST SESSION OF THE TENTH CONGRESS,
ADJOURNED APRIL 25, 1808.

PRESENTED BY
THE NATIONAL CAPITAL SESQUICENTENNIAL COMMISSION
1951

NEG. NO. 11681

THE FIRST SENATE CHAMBER
Placed 1952, bronze 28¼″ x 24″
Original Center building, Senate wing, first floor

NEG. NO. 138

SPEAKER'S PLAQUE
Design: Paul W. Bartlett
Text: by Charles E. Fairman
Placed 1924, bronze, 12″ x 17″
Speaker's Lobby

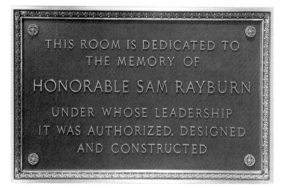

NEG. NO. 22664

SPEAKER SAM RAYBURN
Placed July 6, 1962, bronze, 15¾″ x 24¾″
House Reception Room, H–207

NEG. NO. 1004

TELEGRAPH CENTENNIAL
Sculptor: Lee Lawrie, bronze, 34¾″ x 48¾″
Unveiled May 24, 1944
Center section, first floor

NEG. NO. 24664

PRESIDENTS TREES

Gift: Maryland State Daughters of American Revolution, 1934, bronze on granite
Capitol Grounds, between Louisiana and Delaware Avenues, N.E.

Thirty-one trees were dedicated to 31 United States Presidents by the 31 Maryland Chapters
of Daughters of the American Revolution as part of the Maryland Tercentenary.

NEG. NO. 32197

ARTHUR H. VANDENBERG
Placed March 28, 1967, bronze, 10″ x 14″
S–138

NEG. NO. 24663

GEORGE WASHINGTON'S HOUSES
Gift of District of Columbia, placed during
George Washington Bicentennial, 1932,
bronze on granite
Capitol Plaza fountain terrace

After serving as private homes to successive owners,
the houses became hotels and were in greatly altered
condition when they were razed in 1913.

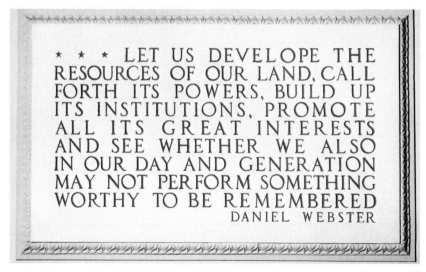

NEG. NO. 17686

QUOTE FROM WEBSTER
Placed House Chamber 1949–50 at the time of its remodeling, marble
Above gallery door, south wall

Source: speech at the laying of the cornerstone of the Bunker Hill Monument at
Charlestown, Boston, Mass. June 17, 1825.

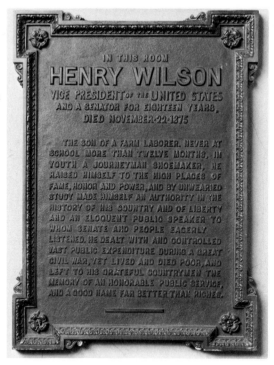

NEG. NO. 25809

HENRY WILSON, VICE PRESIDENT
Placed 1902, bronze, 10½″ x 14½″
Vice President's Room, S–214

NEG. NO. 38902

LINCOLN MARKER
Placed August 1, 1974, bronze, 7½″ x 7½″
Statuary Hall

NEG. NO. 44444

SIGNERS OF THE DECLARATION OF INDEPENDENCE
Sculptor: Alan Robbins, bronze 62″ x 45½″
Accepted by Joint Committee on the Library
Unveiled March 20, 1976
East Front foyer, second floor

# CENTENNIAL SAFE

As a feature of the Centennial Exposition in 1876 in Philadelphia, this safe was displayed as a patriotic gesture by Mrs. Charles F. Deihm, a publisher from New York. In it was placed a diversified collection of pictures and signatures of legislative, judicial, executive, business and civic leaders. Also included were memorabilia such as a silver Tiffany inkstand.

From Philadelphia the safe was brought to Washington in 1877 and placed in Statuary Hall. It was closed with ceremony on February 22, 1879 with the instructions it was to be opened "by the Chief Magistrate" in 1976. Shortly thereafter, it was placed under the east central portico for safekeeping.

As a feature of the Bicentennial celebration, the safe was opened July 1, 1976 by President Gerald Ford.

NEG. NO. 41169

CENTENNIAL SAFE
Manufactured by the Marvin Safe Company
Gift of Mrs. C. F. Deihm, 50″ x 40″ x 64″
Accepted by H. Con. Res. 84, 93d Congress

# Appendix II

Works of Art Property of Committees
Works of Art Transferred
Works of Art Lost in Fires
Works of Art not Part of the Capitol Collection

# WORKS OF ART PROPERTY OF COMMITTEES

NO PHOTOGRAPHS

With the exception of the House Appropriations Committee portraits, works of art acquired by the House and Senate Committees are not part of the Capitol collection. No records of them are maintained in the Office of the Architect of the Capitol, and as a result, this is only a partial listing.

House Agriculture Committee, 1301 Longworth House Office Building.

> Harold D. Cooley by Mabel Pugh
> John W. Flannagan by Dalton Shourds
> Hampton P. Fulmer by Dalton Shourds
> Clifford R. Hope by Mabel Pugh
> Marvin Jones by Boris B. Gordon
> W. R. Poage by Victor Lallier

House Armed Services Committee, 2118 Rayburn House Office Building.

> Walter Gresham Andrews, plaster bust by Anna G. Dunbar
> Walter G. Andrews by Robert O. Skemp
> F. Edward Hébert by John C. Parker
> Philip J. Philbin by Emily B. Waite
> Melvin Price by Robert Templeton
> L. Mendel Rivers by M. John Lenhardt
> Dewey J. Short by Percy A. Leason
> Carl Vinson by Lawrence Powers

House Banking and Currency Committee, 2128 Rayburn House Office Building.

> Wright Patman by Victor Lallier
> Brent Spence by Samuel C. Gholson
> Henry B. Steagall by Howard Chandler Christy
> Jesse Paine Wolcott, photograph by Shoaf

House District of Columbia Committee, 1310 Longworth House Office Building.

> Charles C. Diggs, Jr. by Joseph D. Clipper
> Everett M. Dirksen by Gisbert Palmie
> John L. McMillan by Charles E. Hoover
> Mary T. Norton by Elaine Hartley

House Government Operations Committee, 54 Rayburn House Office Building.

> William L. Dawson by Robert B. Williams
> Chester E. Holifield by Lloyd B. Embry

House Interior and Insular Affairs Committee, 1324 Longworth House Office Building.

> Wayne N. Aspinall by Charles J. Fox
> James A. Haley by Thornton Utz

House International Relations Committee, 2170 Rayburn House Office Building.

> Sol Bloom by Howard Chandler Christy
> Robert B. Chiperfield by Lloyd B. Embry
> Charles A. Eaton by Alfred Jonniaux
> Henry D. Flood by M. Hartman
> Thomas S. Gordon
> John Kee by Alfred Jonniaux
> J. Charles Linthicum by Thomas C. Corner
> Samuel Davis McReynolds by Henry Wolf
> Thomas E. Morgan by Victor Lallier
> James P. Richards by Charles C. Tucker

House Interstate and Foreign Commerce Committee, 2123 Rayburn House Office Building.

> Oren Harris by Louis Freund
> Harley O. Staggers by Charles J. Fox
> Charles A. Wolverton by Charles Ricciardi

House Judiciary Committee, 2141 Rayburn House Office Building.

> Emanuel Celler by Joseph Margulies
> George S. Graham by Richard L. Partington
> Hatton W. Sumners by Boris B. Gordon
> Francis Thomas, photograph

House Merchant Marine and Fisheries Committee, 1334 Longworth House Office Building.

> Schuyler O. Bland by Sandor C. Klein
> Herbert C. Bonner by Mabel Pugh
> Edward A. Garmatz by Charles J. Fox
> Leonor K. Sullivan by Charles J. Fox

House Public Works Committee, 2167 Rayburn House Office Building.

Theodore E. Burton, plaster bust by Louise K. Sparrow
John A. Blatnik by William F. Draper
Charles A. Buckley by Osk Gruber
George A. Dondero by Dorothy H. Drew
George H. Fallon by Charles J. Fox
Robert E. Jones by Charles J. Fox
Joseph J. Mansfield by Boris B. Gordon
William M. Whittington by Karl Wolfe

House Rules Committee, H–313, Capitol.

Ray J. Madden by William J. Sabol
Howard V. Smith by Victor Lallier

House Science and Technology Committee, 2318 Rayburn House Office Building.

George P. Miller by Victor Lallier
Robert H. Goddard by Peter Stevens. Gift of National Space Club
Olin E. Teague by Terry Rodgers

House Small Business Committee, 2359 Rayburn House Office Building. The portraits are the work of artist Lloyd B. Embry.

Joseph L. Evins
William S. Hill
Wright Patman
Walter C. Ploeser

House Veterans' Affairs Committee, 334 Cannon House Office Building.

William J. Bryan Dorn by Robert B. Williams
Royal C. Johnson by Margaret Brisbine

John E. Rankin by Margaret Brisbine
Ray Roberts by Robert B. Williams
Edith N. Rogers by Howard C. Christy
Olin E. Teague by Ralph Chase

House Ways and Means Committee, 1102 Longworth House Office Building.

James W. Collier by Boris B. Gordon
Jere Cooper by Boris B. Gordon
Nelson Dingley, Jr. by unknown artist
Robert L. Doughton by Boris B. Gordon
Robert L. Doughton, photograph tinted in oil
Joseph W. Fordney, photograph tinted in oil
William R. Green by unknown artist
Willis C. Hawley by Boris B. Gordon
Claude Kitchen by Freeman Thorp
Harold Knutson by Thomas E. Stephens
William McKinley, Jr. by Freeman Thorp
Roger Q. Mills by unknown artist
Wilbur D. Mills by Boris B. Gordon
Sereno E. Payne by Cecilia Beaux
Daniel A. Reed by Jean Spencer
Oscar W. Underwood by Michel Jacobs

Albert Thomas Gymnasium, Rayburn House Office Building.

Albert Thomas by Victor Lallier

Senate Armed Services Committee, 212 Russell Senate Office Building.

Iwo Jima by Joseph Capolino

Senate Post Office and Civil Service Committee, 6200 Dirksen Senate Office Building.

Olin Johnston by Frank J. Crawford

## House Republican Leaders

Charles A. Halleck
William J. Sabol, 1974
Signed l.r. Sabol
Gift of friends
Accepted by H. Res. 1477, 93rd Congress and the Joint Committee on the Library
H–227. No photograph

Leslie C. Arends
Signed 1.1. Everett Raymond Kinstler 1977; 38″ x 34″
Gift of friends
Accepted by H. Res. 1544, 94th Congress
H–227. No photograph

NEG. NO. 22469

CRYSTAL CHANDELIER

Transferred from the White House 1902–03. It hung in the Senate connecting corridor, second floor, until June 1962 when it was lent to the White House.

Courtesy Smithsonian Institution

JOSEPH HENRY
Henry Ulke

Transferred to Smithsonian Institution, 1917 by
Senate Resolution 334, 64th Congress

Courtesy Smithsonian Institution

BENJAMIN WEST
Self portrait
Purchased 1876

Transferred to Smithsonian Institution, 1917 by direction of the Joint Committee on the Library

## MEDALS

About 1200 were damaged but not destroyed by the fire of 1851 in the Library of Congress, which was then in
the Capitol. Joint Committee on the Library authorized the Librarian to present the medals to the Smithsonian
Institution July 19, 1861. No photograph.

Courtesy of Department of Interior

CHASM OF THE COLORADO
Thomas Moran, 12' x 6'11''
Purchased 1874
  Transferred 1950 to the Department of Interior P.L. 603, 81st Congress

Courtesy Department of Interior

GRAND CANYON OF THE YELLOWSTONE
Thomas Moran, 11'11'' x 6'10''
Purchased 1872
  Transferred 1950 to the Department of Interior P. L. 603, 81st Congress

NEG. NO. 26185
Courtesy Virginia Military Institute

GENERAL WINFIELD SCOTT
Edward Troye
Purchased 1891

Indefinite loan to Virginia Military Institute 1939, Public Resolution 21,
76th Congress

FARMING IN THE DAKOTAS
Carl Gutherz
Purchased March 3, 1887

Transferred to the Department of Agriculture, 1888
by direction of the Joint Committee on the Library
No photograph

FIRST FIGHT OF THE IRONCLADS
William Formby Halsall
Purchased 1887

Transferred to the United States Naval Academy
Annapolis, Maryland, 1946 by provision of P.L. 700
79th Congress. No photograph

NEG. NO. 10421

FREEDOM, model
Thomas Crawford, plaster, 1858

    Transferred to Smithsonian Institution, 1890
Stored by Smithsonian, 1967

NEG. NO. 25972

IL PENSEROSO
Joseph Mozier, marble, 1872

    Transferred 1888 by direction of the Joint Committee
on the Library to the National Museum, now the National Collection of Fine Arts, Smithsonian Institution.

NEG. NO. 5024

TRIPOLI OR PEACE MONUMENT
Charles Micali, marble

Gift of Officers of the United States Navy to memorialize the losses of the Navy at Tripoli, 1803. Originally placed in the Navy Yard in Washington in 1808; moved to the west grounds of the Capitol 1831. Transferred to the United States Naval Academy at Annapolis, Maryland, 1860 (U.S. Stats. at Large, v. 12, p. 83).

NEG. NO. 144

GEORGE WASHINGTON
Horatio Greenough, marble
Purchased 1833–36
Transferred to Smithsonian Institution 1908 by Pub. Res. No. 26

Installed in the Rotunda 1841 and moved to the east Capitol Grounds, 1844. The huge base became the cornerstone of the Capitol Power Plant.

410

GEORGE WASHINGTON.

The General Assembly of the Commonwealth
of Virginia have caused this Statue to be erected
as a monument of affection and gratitude to
GEORGE WASHINGTON:
who, uniting to the endowments of the *Hero*
the virtues of the *Patriot*, and exerting both
in establishing the Liberties of his Country
has rendered his name dear to his Fellow Citizens.
and given the world an immortal example
of true *Glory*. Done, in the year of
*CHRIST*.
One thousand seven hundred and eighty eight,
and in the year of the Commonwealth the twelfth.

NEG. NO. 148

GEORGE WASHINGTON
William J. Hubard after Antoine Houdon, plaster
Placed in 1850, accepted by Act of July 15, 1870

Transferred by P. L. 605, 81st Congress, July 11, 1950, to Smithsonian Institution.

411

# WORKS OF ART LOST IN FIRES

Three major fires in the Capitol have caused the destruction of works of art. During the War of 1812 the British burned the Capitol on August 24, 1814. Furniture, books from the Library of Congress, paintings, portraits and sculpture were piled in the House and Senate Chambers and then put "to the torch."

The Library of Congress (in the Capitol from 1800 to 1897) was almost totally destroyed by an accidental fire December 24, 1851. Over three fifths of the books were burned and many paintings, portraits and busts were lost.

A fire on January 3, 1930 in a room used to make and store models caused some additional losses.

The accompanying chart is a composite listing of known items that are traditionally recorded as destroyed by fires, although the extant records are incomplete.

| Subject | Item | Artist | Fire |
|---|---|---|---|
| John Adams [2] | Portrait | Gilbert Stuart | 1851 |
| John Quincy Adams | Bust | Luigi Persico | 1851 |
| John Quincy Adams | Portrait | J. Cranch | 1851 |
| Apollo | Bust or statue | Unknown artist | 1851 |
| Samuel Blodget, Jr. | Portrait | John Trumbull (?) | 1930 |
| Simon Bolivar | Portrait | Unknown artist | 1851 |
| Pietro Bonanni | Portrait | Self | 1930 |
| Christopher Columbus | Portraits (2) | Unknown artists | 1851 |
| Christopher Columbus | Bust | Giuseppe Ceracchi | 1851 |
| Hernando Cortez | Portrait | Unknown artist | 1851 |
| Baron De Kalb | Portrait | Unknown artist | 1851 |
| Judge C. D. Drake | Portrait | Charles Bittinger | 1930 |
| John Hanson | Portrait | Unknown artist | 1851 |
| F. Hapler | Bust, plaster | Unknown artist | 1851 |
| Ferdinand R. Hassler | Bust | Unknown artist | 1851 |
| Andrew Jackson | Bust, plaster | Unknown artist | 1851 |
| Thomas Jefferson | Bust, marble | Giuseppe Ceracchi | 1851 |
| Thomas Jefferson [2] | Portrait | Gilbert Stuart | 1851 |
| Thomas Jefferson | Statue | Unknown artist | 1851 |
| William Johnson | Portrait | Unknown artist | 1851 |
| Marquis de Lafayette | Bust, marble | David d'Angers | 1851 |
| Liberty and the Eagle | Statue | Giuseppe Franzoni | 1814 |
| Louis XVI [1] | Portrait | Madame Vigee Lebrun | 1814 |
| James Madison | Medallion | Unknown artist | 1851 |
| James Madison [2] | Portrait | Gilbert Stuart | 1851 |
| Marie Antoinette [1] | Portrait | Madame Vigee Lebrun | 1814 |
| John Marshall | Bust, plaster | Unknown artist | 1851 |
| James Monroe [2] | Portrait | Gilbert Stuart | 1851 |
| Governor Moultrie | Bust, plaster | Col. J. S. Cogdell | 1851 |
| Ogdall | Bust, plaster | Unknown artist | 1851 |
| Peyton Randolph | Portrait | Unknown artist | 1851 |
| Zachary Taylor | Bust, marble | Unknown artist | 1851 |
| Americus Vespucius | Bust | Giuseppe Ceracchi | 1851 |
| Baron Von Steuben | Portrait | Pyne | 1851 |
| George Washington | Bust | Giuseppe Ceracchi | 1851 |
| George Washington | Bust, bronze | David d'Angers | 1851 |
| George Washington [2] | Portrait | Gilbert Stuart | 1851 |
| L. Woodbury | Bust, plaster | Unknown artist | 1851 |

[1] These portraits disappeared in 1814, but it is not known whether they were burned or sent out prior to the fire to be repaired and were never returned.

[2] Owned by Mr. Phelps of Boston.

# WORKS OF ART NOT PART OF THE CAPITOL COLLECTION

The Joint Committee on the Library has not accepted these works of art. Some are gifts, some have been left by owners who cannot be located. Any existing records are maintained by the Architect of the Capitol. For many, the records are incomplete or the works cannot be found.

| Subject | Item | Artist | Location |
|---|---|---|---|
| Jean Louis R. Agassiz, Swiss-American naturalist | Portrait | Henry Ulke | Location unknown, Purchased 1877 |
| Harold R. Beckley, Superintendent of Senate Press Gallery | Photograph tinted in oil | Gladys A. Kazigian | Press Room, Dirksen Office Building. Gift from Correspondents' Committee. |
| Theodore E. Burton, Representative and Senator from Ohio | Bust, plaster | Louise Kidder Sparrow | In storage Gift of the artist, |
| Archibald Willingham Butt, Major, United States Army | Portrait, 40″ x 60″ | Harold L. Macdonald about 1923 | In storage No records |
| Joseph G. Cannon, Speaker of the House of Representatives | Portrait | Michel Jacobs | 244 Cannon House Office Building |
| Joseph G. Cannon | Portrait | George Burroughs Torrey | In storage |
| Carpenter's Hall | Painting, 38⅜″ x 50⅜″ | Charles McVickers, 1967 | HB–29. Presented to House of Representatives September 25, 1974 by U.S. Capitol Historical Society. |
| Subject unknown. Sometimes referred to as Columbus | Bust, plaster 29½″ | Unknown artist | HB–28 No records |
| Downwind Victory | Painting, 25⅜″ x 30⅜″ | Bruce E. Roberts, 1973 | H–125. Gift of artist to House of Representatives May 10, 1973 |
| Charles E. Fairman, First Art Curator of the Capitol | Portrait 24½″ x 29½″ | Nicholas R. Brewer | HB–28. Gift of Mr. Fairman |
| Flowers of Joy | Painting 35½″ x 47½″ | Beatrice Van Wye | H–311. Presented to House of Representatives May 15, 1968 in honor of Congressional wives. Accepted by Speaker John W. McCormack |
| Thomas Hendricks, Representative and Senator from Indiana and Vice President | Portrait | Unknown artist | Location unknown |
| Abraham Lincoln | Bust, bronze | Unknown artist | Location unknown Gift of Col. A. DeGroot, 1871 |
| Abraham Lincoln | Portrait | Griswold Tyng | S–113. Gift of Senator Kenneth S. Wherry's family, 1952 |

| Subject | Item | Artist | Location |
|---------|------|--------|----------|
| John T. Morgan<br>  Senator from Alabama | Portrait | Carl Gutherz, 1893 | S–339. Offered by Senator Morgan's daughter, 1910 |
| Justin Morrill<br>  Representative and Senator from<br>  Vermont | Portrait | Carl Gutherz | Location unknown |
| Franklin Delano Roosevelt | Portrait | Unknown artist | In storage. Presented by National Italian American Civic League, 1937 |
| Seascape | Painting,<br>  30″ x 50″ | John D. Wisinski | H–130. Gift of Representative John C. Kluczynski to House of Representatives January 26, 1972. Accepted by Speaker Carl Albert |
| Morris Sheppard<br>  Representative and Senator from<br>  Texas | Portrait | B. Godwin, 1939 | In Storage. No records |
| Robert A. Taft<br>  Senator from Ohio | Portrait | Rudolph Bernatschke, 1953 | S–229. Gift of the artist, 1959 |
| Nicholas Van Dyke, Jr.<br>  Senator from Delaware | Portrait | Jefferson D. Chalfant | S–209. Presented to the Senate in 1914 by great granddaughters of Senator Van Dyke |
| Uncle Sam '76 | Statuette, plaster,<br>  21½″ | Attributed to Horatio Stone | HB–28. No records |
| United States Capitol, East Front | Painting, watercolor,<br>  35½″ x 81½″ | Hughson Hawley, 1905 | Corridor, across from SB–15. Purchased 1905 |
| United States Capitol Extension,<br>  East Front | Painting | Robert Kirwan, 1960 | SB–16. Gift of Chesapeake and Potomac Telephone Company, 1961 |
| United States Capitol, West Front | Painting, after an 1840 engraving by Bartlett, 23″ x 28″ | Unknown artist, about 1850 | SB–15. Gift of John C. Stevens, 1946 |
| United States Senate, A.D. 1850 | Engraving | | S–224. Gift of United States Capitol Historical Society, 1964 |
| Victory: U.S.S. Constitution<br>  After the Battle With the<br>  Guerriere | Painting | Gilbert T. Margeson, about 1905 | H–104. No records |
| Thomas J. Walsh<br>  Senator from Montana | Bust, plaster | Louise Kidder Sparrow | Location unknown. Gift of artist |
| Thomas U. Walter<br>  4th Architect of the Capitol. | Portrait | Eloise L. Everson, | In storage. Gift of artist |
| Daniel Webster Addressing the<br>  United States Senate on the<br>  Compromise Measures, March 7,<br>  1850 | Engraving | R. Van Dien, 1856 | HB–28. No records |
| Daniel Webster | Portrait, 23″ x 31″ | Francis H. Cumberland, 1961 | S–146. Gift of artist |

# Appendix III

## Floor Plans

The works of art in this book are located by room numbers and area names. By using the room designations given with each description in the text, their locations in the Capitol may be determined on the following floor plans.

Rooms to the left of the center are in the House wing and their numbers are preceded by an "H". Rooms to the right of the center are in the Senate wing and their numbers are preceded by an "S".

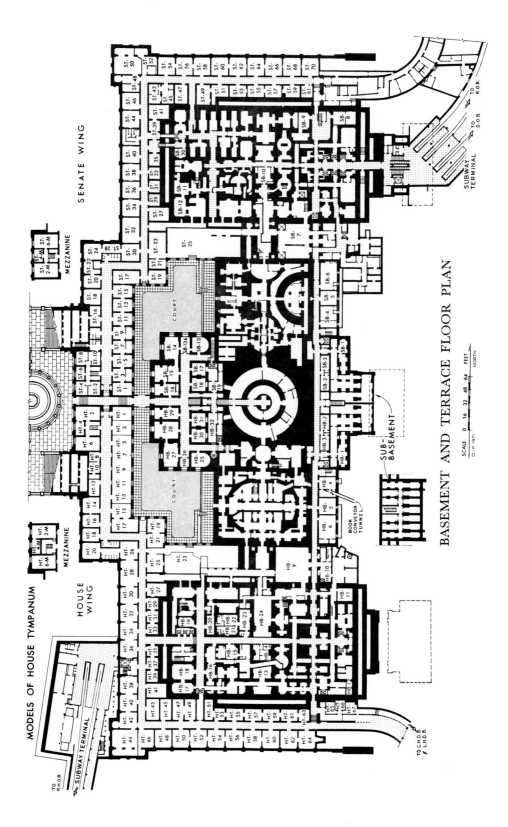

BASEMENT AND TERRACE FLOOR PLAN

SCALE: 0  16  32  48  64  FEET

O.I.P 1971

NORTH

418

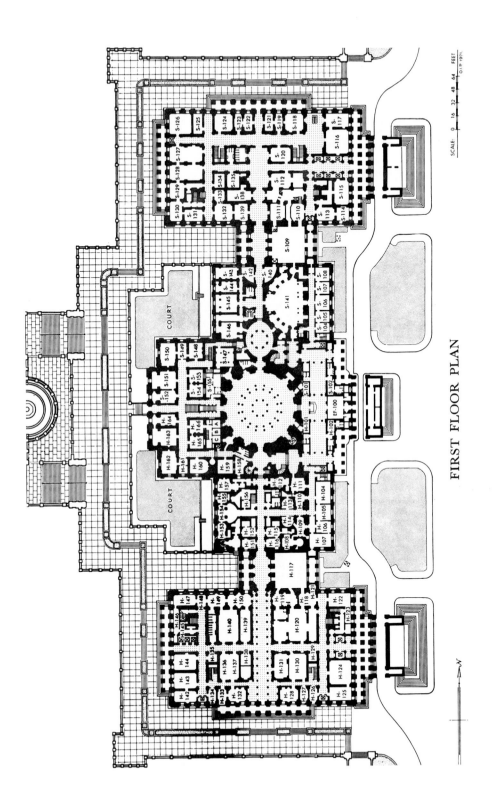

FIRST FLOOR PLAN

SCALE: 0   16   32   48   64   FEET
O.I.P 1971.

N

419

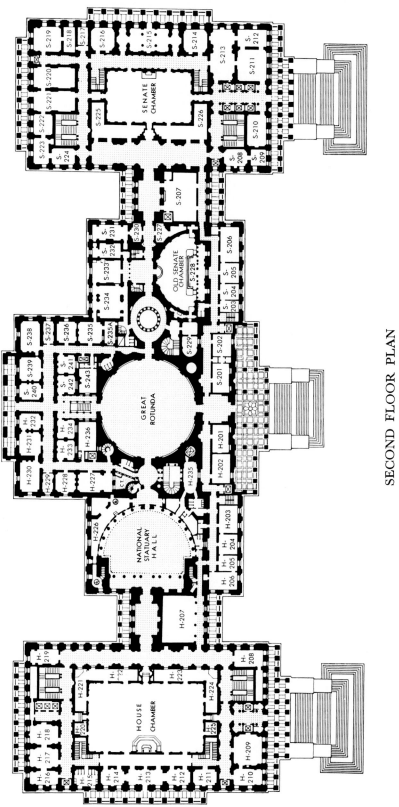

SECOND FLOOR PLAN

scale: 0  16  32  48  64  feet
O·I·P 1971        NORTH

420

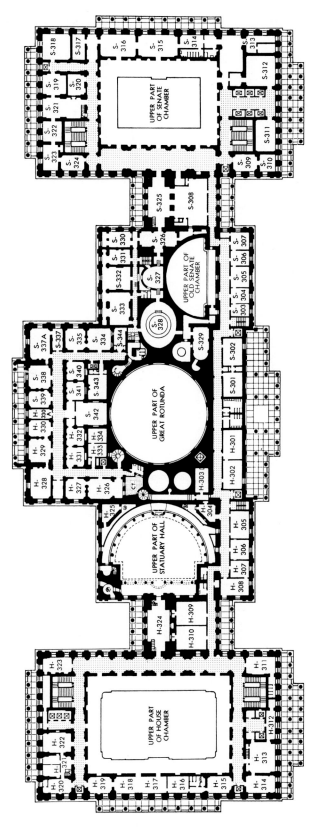

THIRD FLOOR PLAN

scale: 0  16  32  48  64  feet

O.I.P. 1971.          NORTH

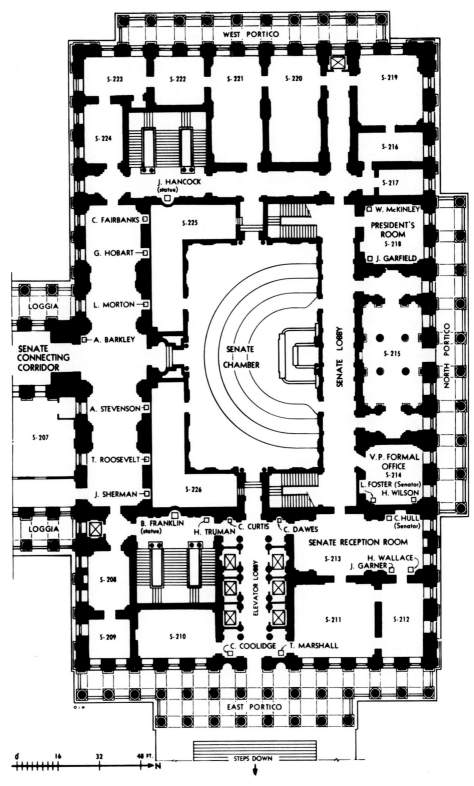

SENATE WING, SECOND FLOOR, SHOWING LOCATIONS OF BUSTS AND STATUES

422

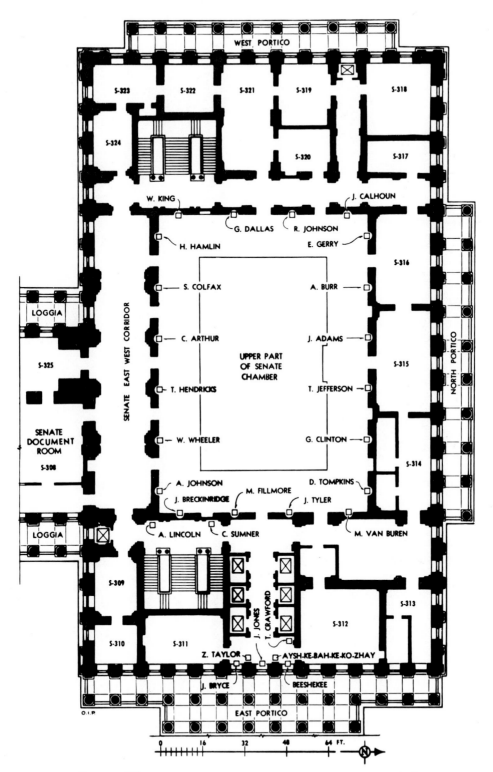

SENATE WING, THIRD FLOOR, SHOWING LOCATIONS OF BUSTS

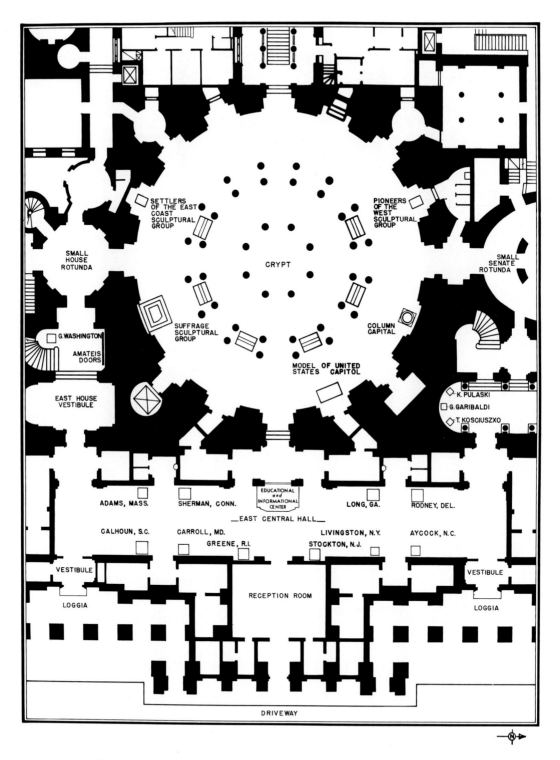

CRYPT, FIRST FLOOR, SHOWING LOCATION OF STATUARY AND BUSTS

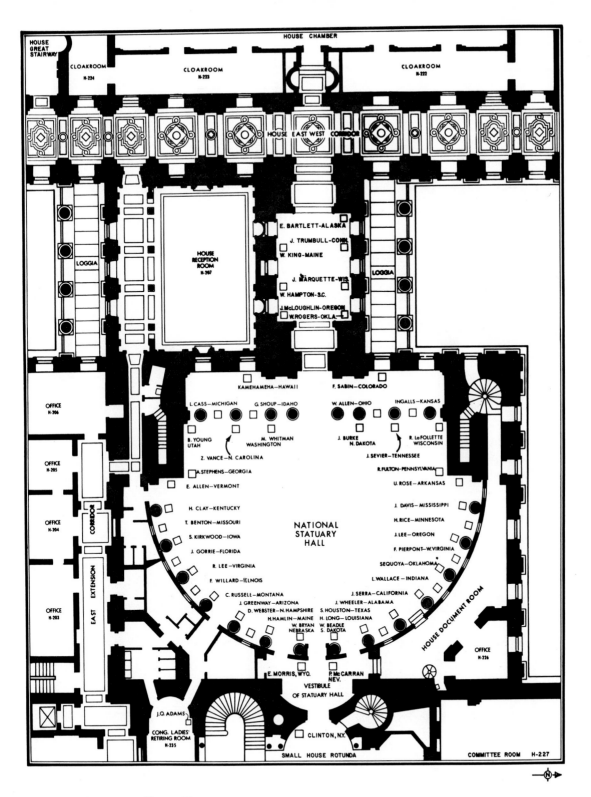

NATIONAL STATUARY HALL, HOUSE WING, SECOND FLOOR, SHOWING LOCATIONS OF STATUES IN THE HALL, THE ADJACENT CONNECTING CORRIDOR AND THE SMALL HOUSE ROTUNDA

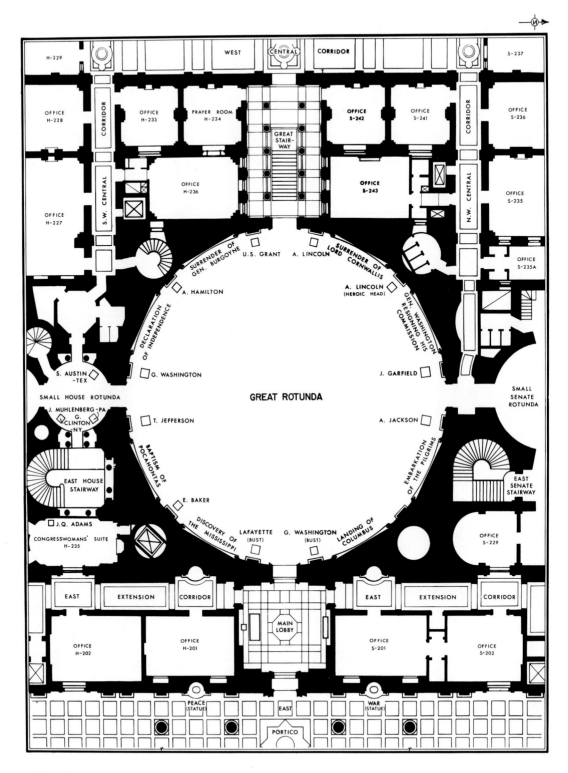

THE ROTUNDA, SECOND FLOOR, SHOWING LOCATIONS OF PAINTINGS, STATUES AND BUSTS

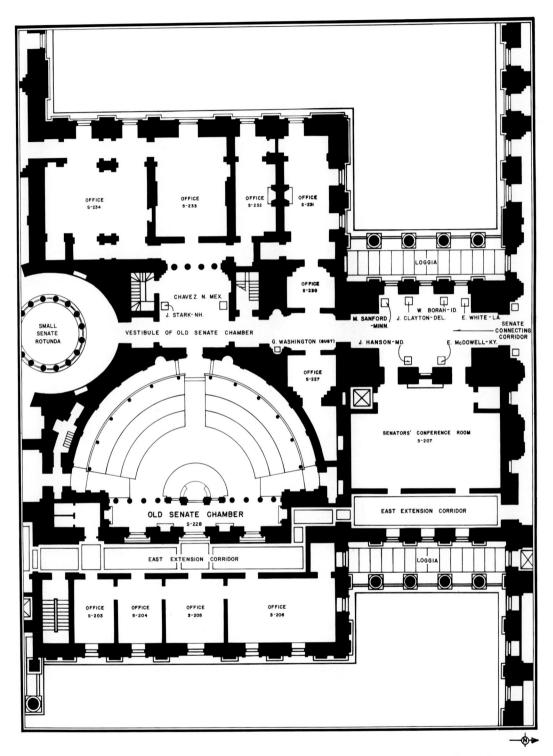

OLD SENATE WING, SECOND FLOOR, SHOWING THE STATUES IN THE STATUARY HALL COLLECTION

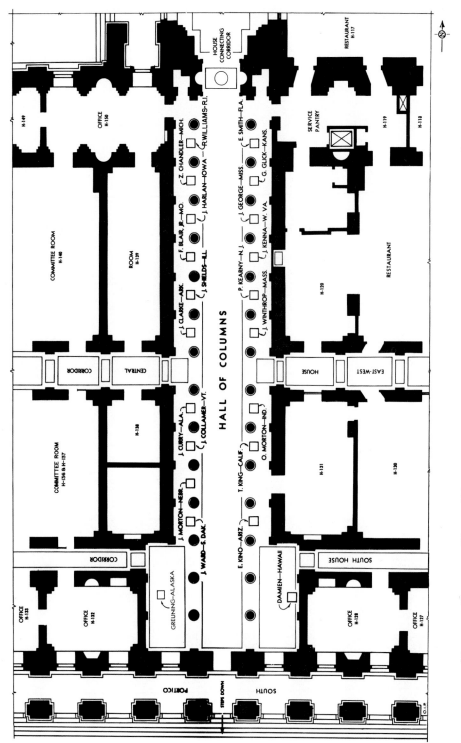

HALL OF COLUMNS, HOUSE WING, FIRST FLOOR, SHOWING LOCATIONS OF STATUES IN THE STATUARY
HALL COLLECTION

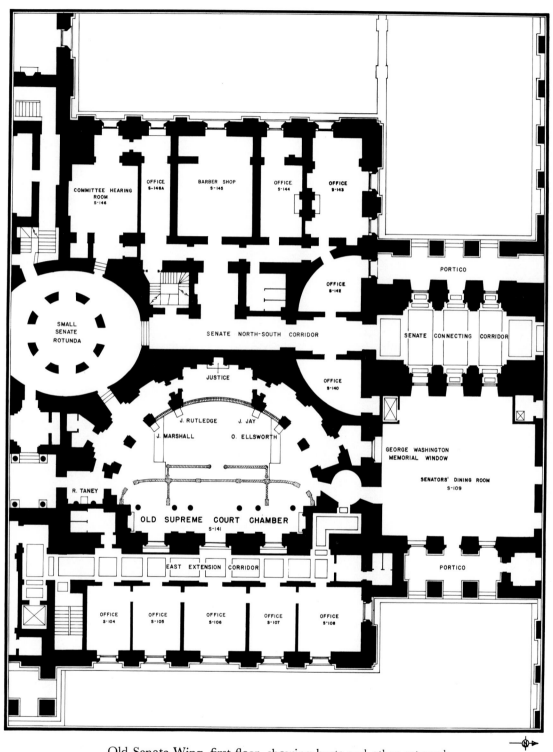

Old Senate Wing, first floor, showing busts and other art work

# INDEX

Illustrations are indicated in bold face type

431

436

441

444

445

447

449

450

☆ U. S. GOVERNMENT PRINTING OFFICE : 1978 O - 78-299